HIGH NOON

IDENTIFYING THE SEQUENCE • IDENTIFYING DETAILS

READING

UNDERSTANDING THE MAIN IDEA • USING CONTEXT

COMPREHENSION

DRAWING CONCLUSIONS • MAKING INFERENCES

LEVEL D

Deborah Akers

HIGH NOON BOOKS

Available from High Noon Books

High Noon Reading Comprehension Program
Level A ISBN 1-57128-186-X
Level B ISBN 1-57128-187-8
Level C ISBN 1-57128-188-6
Level D ISBN 1-57128-189-4

Cover Design by Lucy Neilson

High Noon Books
A division of Academic Therapy Publications
20 Commercial Boulevard
Novato, CA 94949-6191
800-422-7249

International Standard Book Number 1-57128-189-4
ISBN 13: 978-1-57128-189-0

19 18 17 16 15 14 13 12 11 10
13 12 11 10 09 08 07 06 05 04

TABLE OF CONTENTS

TO THE TEACHER

High Noon Reading Comprehension is designed to give your students strategies and opportunities for practice that will improve their reading comprehension skills.

Program Features

Each unit contains a series of six lessons that provide the following elements:

- Grade 4 reading level
- Unit opener comprehension strategies lesson
- Vocabulary lessons
- Reading passages that gradually increase in length
- A range of high-interest topics from a variety of genres and subject areas
- Review lessons at the end of each unit

How to Use These Lessons

Provide students with a copy of the Answer Sheet found on page 78 of this book. As students become familiar with the format of the book, lessons may be completed independently. However, specific direct explanations of strategies, modeling, guided practice, and feedback will support your students' efforts and can contribute significantly to their success.

Strategy Lessons. For the first lesson of each unit, read together the unit opener strategy lesson. Discussing the strategies and answering students' questions at this stage will help them prepare to read strategically.

Vocabulary Words. Specific discussion of the words listed in each lesson may be beneficial.

1. Write the vocabulary words on the board.
2. Assist students with any difficult pronunciations.
3. Read together the example sentences and discuss the meaning of each word.
4. Ask students to use each word in a sentence. Write that sentence on the board.

Modeling Reading. You can demonstrate how to use a strategy by modeling the process of strategic reading. Read aloud the first few lines of a passage, asking questions as you read to reinforce comprehension.

Guided Practice. Ask students to read the first paragraph or the first few sentences of the selection. Discuss what they have read in light of the lesson's strategy focus.

Feedback. When the students have completed a lesson, answers can be checked with the Answer Key on pages 79-80. The number correct can be entered on the Progress Chart found on the Answer Sheet. Take the opportunity to review items missed at this point and return to the lesson for further instruction if necessary.

Reading is a very important skill. It helps you learn about many new things. You can learn about almost anything by reading about it. You can learn more about sports and animals. You can learn about how to make things. You can enjoy a good adventure story. Reading opens up the world.

Good readers use tricks, or "strategies," to help them understand what they read. The strategies you will learn in this book are—

- Identifying the Sequence
- Identifying Details
- Using the Context
- Understanding the Main Idea
- Drawing Conclusions
- Using Inference

How to Use This Book

- Your teacher will help you decide which skills you need to practice. For each unit go to the first lesson. Read the strategies. Then read the vocabulary words. Ask questions if there are words you do not understand.

- Follow the directions and read the passages. Remember to think about what you are reading.

- Answer the questions after each passage. Mark your answers on the Answer Sheet.

- When you are done with the lesson, check your answers with the Answer Key.

- Record how many answers you got right on the Progress Chart.

This book is meant to help you become a better reader. Think about the strategies you learn. Also enjoy the stories. Don't worry if you miss some of the questions. The important thing is to do your best. Reading takes practice, just like sports. The more you practice, the better you'll get and the more you'll enjoy reading!

UNIT 1
LESSON 1

Skill Focus: Identifying the Sequence

In a selection, things happen in a certain order. This is called sequence. Knowing the sequence will help you understand what you read. Here are some clues to help you:

- Read carefully.
- Look for words like *first, last, next, then, before,* and *after.*
- Think about time clues in what you read. These are words like *hours, days, months,* and *years.*
- Think about the order that makes the most sense in what you read.

VOCABULARY

instant . . . . . all at once
season . . . . . a period of time

streak . . . . shoot through the air very fast

Read each passage. Then choose the correct answer for each question.

THE INSTANT GARDEN

Jon got some flower bulbs in the mail. "What will I do with these?" he said.

He dug a hole in the backyard. Then he threw in the bulbs. He put the dirt back, then he forgot about them.

That spring, Jon had an instant garden. Beautiful flowers bloomed all season.

1 What happened first?

    A. Jon forgot about the bulbs.
    B. The bulbs came in the mail.
    C. Jon dug a hole.
    D. Jon put the bulbs in the ground.

2 What happened last?

    A. Jon forgot about the bulbs.
    B. The flower bulbs came in the mail.
    C. Jon dug a hole in the backyard.
    D. The bulbs bloomed into flowers.

FINDING THE STARS

Becky was studying the stars. She had all sorts of books and maps. One night, she decided to look at the stars for herself. She sat on a blanket and looked up at the sky. There was the North Star! Then Becky saw a shooting star streak through the sky.

3 What happened first?

A. Becky studied books on stars.
B. Becky went outside at night.
C. Becky saw a shooting star.
D. Becky saw the North star.

4 What happened last?

A. Becky found the North Star.
B. Becky saw a shooting star.
C. Becky went outside at night.
D. Becky read books on the stars.

MARIA'S GARAGE

Maria loves to fix cars. She used to help out in her dad's auto repair shop after school.

Now Maria has her own repair shop. She has plants and paintings in the office. People like Maria's shop. It is a nice place to be, and Maria does a great job on their cars.

5 What happened first?

A. Maria opened up her own shop.
B. Maria worked with her dad.
C. Maria works on people's cars.
D. Maria put plants in her office.

6 What happened last?

A. Maria did not want to work on cars.
B. Maria worked with her dad.
C. Maria grew up.
D. Maria opened up her own shop.

LILY'S BATH

Lily the dog didn't like getting a bath. Her owner, Terry, had a plan. First, he took Lily out on a hot day. Next, they played ball for a while. Soon, Lily got hot. At last, Terry turned on the water hose. Lily was happy to get a good washing.

7 What happened first?

A. Lily got a bath.
B. Terry turned on the hose.
C. Lily and Terry went out in the yard.
D. Terry and Lily played ball.

8 What happened last?

A. Lily and Terry played ball.
B. Lily got a bath outside.
C. It was hot outside.
D. Lily did not want a bath.

SKATING HOME

Milton decided that he would skate home from his friend's house. But Milton's house was more than 500 miles away! At first, he took the back roads. He also got a few rides. He got home three weeks later.

9 What happened first?

A. Milton took the back roads.
B. Milton went to see a friend.
C. Milton got a few rides.
D. Milton got home three weeks later.

10 What happened last?

A. Milton took back roads.
B. Milton visited his friend.
C. Milton got home three weeks later.
D. Milton worked on his skates.

Now use the Answer Key to check your answers. Mark the number you got correct on the Progress Chart.

LESSON 2

VOCABULARY

climate . . . . . . the weather
buttery . . . . . . looks like butter
performance . . . an act

antics . . . . funny tricks
barrier . . . . something that blocks

Read each passage. Then choose the correct answer for each question.

THE NEW BAT

The baseball season was starting. Marta hoped that this would be the year that she hit her first home run. But first, she needed a new bat. She went down to Mel's Baseball Mart. "I'm looking for just the right baseball bat," she told Mel.

Mel grabbed a bat. "Give this a try."

Marta took the bat outside. First, she threw a ball in the air. Then she swung. CRRACK! The ball sailed up over the store. Marta ran inside. "I'll take the bat!" she said.

1 What happened first?

   A. Marta hit the ball very hard.
   B. Marta said she would take the bat.
   C. Mel brought out a big baseball bat.
   D. Marta went to Mel's Baseball Mart.

2 What happened last?

   A. The ball sailed over the store.
   B. Baseball season had come.
   C. Marta ran inside the store.
   D. Marta hit the ball hard.

MAKING CHOCOLATE

It is easy to eat a chocolate bar. It is much harder to make the chocolate that goes in the candy bar. Chocolate fruits grow on trees in countries where the climate is hot. The fruits grow as big as bowling balls. Then workers cut them down. They take off the shells and let the chocolate beans dry. Then the beans are cleaned. Then they are crushed in a machine. A buttery paste comes out. That is the stuff that is used to make chocolate.

3 What happens first?

   A. The beans are dried.
   B. The beans are cut down.
   C. You eat the candy bar.
   D. The beans are crushed.

4 What happens last?

   A. The beans are cut down.
   B. The beans are dried.
   C. The beans are crushed.
   D. A buttery paste is made.

THE PARADE

Sarah was looking for her sister, Leah, in the big parade. Leah and her acting club were going to do a special performance in the parade. But Leah wouldn't tell Sarah what it was. First, a marching band played. Then some kids on horses trotted by. After that, some people came running along. They were all dressed like chickens. They did all sorts of silly antics. Everyone clapped.

After the parade was over, one of the chickens came over and hugged Sarah. It was Leah! "Did you recognize me?" she asked. Sarah laughed and hugged her back.

5 What came first in the parade?

   A. A marching band.
   B. The tractors.
   C. The chickens.
   D. The kids on horses.

6 What came next?

   A. Sarah and Leah.
   B. A marching band.
   C. Kids on horses.
   D. The chickens.

7 What happened last?

   A. Sarah was looking for Leah.
   B. Leah came up in her chicken suit.
   C. Leah was not in the parade.
   D. The parade started.

THE SECRET OF FLYING

Everyone knows that birds have wings. That's how they fly. But do you know how the wings actually fly? Here's how it works. First, the bird lifts its wings upward. When it does this, the bird's feathers press tightly together. When the wings are fully raised, the feathers form a barrier. No air can pass between them. Then the bird moves its wings downward. Finally, the bird can move forward.

8 What happens first?

   A. The bird moves forward.
   B. The bird moves its wings up.
   C. The bird moves its wings down.
   D. The bird eats dinner.

9 What happens next?

   A. The wind gets trapped in the feathers.
   B. The bird moves its wings up.
   C. The bird lands on the ground.
   D. The bird learns to fly.

10 What happens last?

   A. The bird has feathers.
   B. The bird moves its wings down.
   C. The bird moves its feathers.
   D. The bird moves forward.

Now use the Answer Key to check your answers. Mark the number you got correct on the Progress Chart.

UNIT 1
LESSON 3

VOCABULARY

archeologist .. someone who digs up old objects

ingredients ... things you put together when cooking

artifacts ..... very old things

mixture ...... things that are mixed together

Read each passage. Then choose the correct answer for each question.

LEFT BEHIND

A tall man raced along the beach. "Wait for me!" he called. "I've changed my mind!"

The man was Alexander Selkirk. He was calling to a ship. Before, he had decided he wanted to stay on the island. The boat would leave him there. He changed his mind at the last minute just as the ship sailed away. It was too late.

Selkirk lived on the island for four years. He lived in a cave and washed in a stream. He hunted, gathered fruit, and fished for his food. He always kept looking for another ship.

Finally, another ship came. Selkirk went home and told about his adventure. Someone wrote a story about it. The book is called Robinson Crusoe.

1 What happened first?

    A. Another ship came along.
    B. The boat left the island.
    C. Selkirk lived in a cave.
    D. Selkirk wrote a story.

2 When happened next?

    A. The boat left the island.
    B. Selkirk told his story.
    C. Selkirk gathered food.
    D. Another ship came.

3 What happened last?

    A. Selkirk gathered food.
    B. Selkirk told his story.
    C. Selkirk was alone.
    D. Selkirk lived in a cave.

DIGGING UP ARTIFACTS

Lisa was learning to be an archeologist. She was at her first dig. Dr. Lean, her teacher, showed her how to start.

First, they ran a rope around a small piece of ground. They could see a few old pots sticking out of the ground. They knelt down by the pots But they didn't pick up the pots yet. They took out tiny shovels. They started to dig around the pots carefully. They tried not to touch the pots with their shovels. They dug down until each pot was uncovered. Only then did they carefully pick them up.

4 What did Dr. Lean and Lisa do first?

    A. Picked up pots.
    B. Dug with their shovels.
    C. Roped off the area.
    D. Read books about pots.

5 What did they do next?

    A. Roped off the area.
    B. Learned to read.
    C. Picked up the pots.
    D. Dug around the pots carefully.

6 What did they do last?

    A. Picked up the pots carefully.
    B. Dug around the pots carefully.
    C. Read about their pots.
    D. Roped off the area.

MAKING A SMOOTHIE

Do you like smoothies? They are tasty, and good for you, too. They are also easy to make. First, make sure you have a blender. It should have a strong motor. Then choose your favorite fruits. You can use apples, berries, peaches, or even mangoes! You should also add a banana. If you like ice cream or yogurt, you can add some. Put all the ingredients in the blender. Blend it until it is a smooth mixture. If it is too thick, add a little bit of juice. Then enjoy your smoothie. It's an easy way to get lots of vitamins and minerals.

7 When you make a smoothie, what should you do first?

    A. Put in some juice.
    B. Get out your blender.
    C. Choose your favorite fruits.
    D. Enjoy your smoothie.

8 What should you do next?

    A. Choose which fruits you want to use.
    B. Make sure you have a good blender.
    C. Get lots of vitamins and minerals.
    D. Blend the fruit.

9 What can you put in after you've blended the smoothie?

    A. Vitamins and minerals.
    B. A little juice.
    C. Your favorite fruits.
    D. A strong motor.

10 What do you do last?

    A. Add some bananas.
    B. Get some fruit.
    C. Enjoy your smoothie.
    D. Get a blender.

Now use the Answer Key to check your answers. Mark the number you got correct on the Progress Chart.

UNIT 1
LESSON 4

VOCABULARY

surviving . . . living through something
adequate . . . enough
nutrients . . . things that nourish

compost . . . . . dirt made of broken down food and leaves

Read each passage. Then choose the correct answer for each question.

GINA'S SHELTER

Gina wanted to make a shelter in the woods. She got some books from the library. She also talked to her grandpa about it. He had been a park ranger in Alaska. He knew everything about surviving outdoors.

Gina and her grandpa went out one Saturday afternoon. They looked around for a good spot to build the shelter. They chose an open field up on a hill. That way, they wouldn't get flooded. They would also get adequate sunlight.

Then they looked for sticks to build the frame. First, they found a thick stick for the top of the roof. That is called the ridgepole. They set one end on the ground. Then they propped the other end on a tree stump. They found other shorter sticks. They leaned those sticks against the ridgepole. It made a sort of tent. Then they covered the frame with lots of leaves, grass, and moss.

Gina and her grandpa did a good job on the shelter. They decided that they would stay overnight in it. They had a warm, snug night of camping.

1 What did Gina do first?

   A. She found the ridgepole.
   B. She went camping.
   C. She talked to her grandpa.
   D. She found a good camping spot.

2 What did Gina and her grandpa do first?

   A. They got a ridgepole for the shelter.
   B. They found a good spot to build.
   C. They read lots of library books.
   D. They went to sleep.

3 What did they do next?

   A. Found a ridgepole.
   B. Went camping.
   C. Leaned short sticks on the ridgepole.
   D. Got some leaves.

4 What did they do after they made the frame?

   A. They climbed a hill.
   B. They got leaves and grass.
   C. They went camping.
   D. Found a good spot to camp.

5 What did they do last?

    A. They found the ridgepole.
    B. They found some leaves.
    C. They stayed overnight.
    D. They went home.

MAKING COMPOST

Compost is another word for dirt. It is soil made from food and leaves that have broken down. Compost has lots of nutrients in it. They help plants and flowers grow well.

It is very easy to make your own compost. First, you need to build a box. It should have high sides and no bottom. One side is attached with hinges, so you can open up the box. You can also make a lid for the box.

After you are done with the box, the rest is easy. Put in some food scraps like apple peels. Then you can pour a little potting soil on top. You can put in things like grass clippings and leaves. You can put in old fruits and vegetables. You can put in coffee grounds or used tea bags. Just don't put in anything like meat, eggs, or cheese. That will attract bugs or animals.

Your pile will get bigger and bigger. When it rains, you can take off the lid. A little water is good for your compost. The material at the bottom will start to break down. By the time your box is filled, the bottom part will be compost. Open the side of the box and shovel the compost out. You can spread it on your garden. You will be happy with the results!

6 When you are making a compost pile, what should you do first?

    A. Put in old fruit.
    B. Shovel the compost.
    C. Plant a garden.
    D. Build a box.

7 What can you do after you finish the box sides?

    A. Plant a garden.
    B. Make a box lid.
    C. Shovel the compost.
    D. Build the box.

8 What should you do after the box is done?

    A. Put food scraps in the box.
    B. Pour water in the box.
    C. Shovel out the compost.
    D. Put food scraps on your garden.

9 What should you do after the box gets full?

    A. Plant a garden with the compost.
    B. Put the lid on the box.
    C. Shovel compost from the bottom.
    D. Put in coffee grounds.

10 What should you do last?

    A. Attract bugs.
    B. Build another box.
    C. Spread the compost.
    D. Plant a garden.

Now use the Answer Key to check your answers. Mark the number you got correct on the Progress Chart.

UNIT 1
LESSON 5

VOCABULARY

decorations . . things you put up to look nice

complicated . . something with many parts

digest . . . . to make food into energy for your body

saliva . . . . fluid in the mouth

Read each passage. Then choose the correct answer for each question.

MAKE YOUR OWN CLAY

Here's a good craft idea. Make a batch of baker's clay. It's a little messy, but a lot of fun.

First get out the ingredients. You will need a cup of flour, a half cup of salt, and half a cup of water. Also get some food coloring and a little bit of oil. You will also need a large pan.

First, mix the flour and salt. Then mix the food coloring with the water. Next, add the water slowly to the flour mixture. Mix it until it feels like clay or play dough. Finally, add the oil to make it smooth.

Now it's time to make shapes with the clay. You can make anything you want. You can make cars or a neat boat with it. You could make holiday decorations to hang up. You can braid the clay. First, roll three small strands of clay. Lay them next to each other. Then braid them together like you do with hair. Try making a breadbasket or a wreath with the braid.

Bake the shapes in the oven at 225 degrees for about 15 minutes. Make sure to use oven mitts when you take them out!

1 When making clay, what do you mix first?

A. Clay and water.
B. Flour and salt.
C. Water and oil.
D. A baking pan.

2 What do you mix next?

A. A baking pan.
B. Flour and salt.
C. Water and oil.
D. Water and color.

3 What do you do after you mix the ingredients?

A. Get oil and water.
B. Bake the clay.
C. Shape the clay.
D. Get a baking pan.

4 To make a clay braid, what do you do first?

A. Make three small clay rolls.
B. Mix the ingredients.
C. Make a breadbasket.
D. Add color to the clay.

5 After the shapes are done, what do you do next?

    A. Make a breadbasket.
    B. Put them in the oven.
    C. Mix up the clay.
    D. Mix up the flour and salt.

HOW YOUR BODY USES FOOD

Do you know what happens when you eat? You chew, swallow, and then the food goes into your stomach. But it is more complicated than that. Your body does many things to help you digest your food.

The process starts when you put food in your mouth. Your mouth has saliva in it. The saliva mixes with the food and makes it soft. That helps you swallow. When the food goes to your stomach, it turns around and around. Fluids in your stomach help the food turn into a liquid. The liquid goes to different organs in your body.

Each organ has a special job. The intestine takes the good parts of the food. It sends the nutrients into your blood. Your blood takes them where they are needed in the body. The liver gets rid of the parts your body can't use. The kidneys absorb water and salt that your body needs. They also get rid of extra salt.

Your body knows how to get what it needs. And it does all this while you are running or reading or sleeping.

6 What is the first thing that happens when you digest food?

    A. The kidneys absorb it.
    B. The food turns into liquid.
    C. Your liver gets rid of waste.
    D. You chew food in your mouth.

7 What happens next?

    A. The food goes to the stomach.
    B. You get nutrients.
    C. The food goes in your mouth.
    D. The food goes to the kidneys.

8 What happens before food goes to the intestine?

    A. The kidneys absorb it.
    B. It goes into the blood.
    C. It turns into liquid.
    D. It turns into salt.

9 What happens after the liquid goes into the intestine?

    A. It goes into the blood stream.
    B. You chew the food.
    C. It goes to the stomach.
    D. It goes in your mouth.

10 What else happens after the food is turned to liquid?

    A. You chew it up.
    B. You have more to eat.
    C. The kidneys get rid of extra salt.
    D. It goes in your mouth.

Now use the Answer Key to check your answers. Mark the number you got correct on the Progress Chart.

LESSON 6

VOCABULARY

paralyzed . .	cannot move
injuries	harm to the body
disability . . .	loss of powers
cover	report on

interviewed . .	to ask someone questions for a story
obstacles	something that stands in the way

Read the passage. It is about John Hockenberry. Then choose the correct answer for each question.

JOHN HOCKENBERRY

In 1976, John Hockenberry got a ride home from college. He was sitting in the back seat of a car. John fell asleep after awhile. So did the driver of the car. The car went off the road. One person was killed, and John's spine was broken. He was paralyzed from the waist down.

John was in the hospital for many months. His other injuries finally healed, but it was clear that he would never walk again. John began learning to use a wheelchair. When he left the hospital, the world was a different place. At that time, many buildings did not have ramps for wheelchairs. John soon realized that he had many challenges to face.

John went back to college for awhile. Then he quit and tried to get a job as a welder. The company would not give him a job because of the wheelchair. It was not the first time John would run into obstacles. But he never let it get him down.

After that, he went to music school for awhile in Oregon. While in school he got a

reporting job. For the first time, he spoke on the radio. He loved it! John decided he wanted to become a broadcaster.

The boss of his radio station lived in another state. He had never met John. John never told him that he was in a wheelchair. He did not want to be treated any differently. But one day, he missed a deadline. He couldn't call the story in because the wheelchair wouldn't fit in the phone booth. The boss found out what had happened. The boss didn't fire John. He gave him a full-time job instead.

John reported on all sorts of stories in Oregon. Then in 1981, he was offered another job. He would work on a national radio show. John moved to Washington, DC. He started reporting on stories all over the world.

One time, John went to cover a war in the Middle East. He had to travel out in the desert. He had no car, so he got a donkey. He tied himself onto the donkey so he wouldn't fall off. He rode the donkey for miles through the desert. His report on the war was heard all over the United States.

Soon, John was working in television. In 1989, he even had his own show for awhile. He interviewed all sorts of people on the show. John has won many awards for his work.

John has always spoken out for the rights of disabled people. He wrote a book to tell his story. He wanted people to know that having a disability does not have to end your life. For John, it was just a beginning.

1   Which happened first?

A. John went to music school.
B. John went to the Middle East.
C. John was in a bad car accident.
D. John was on TV.

2   What happened first after John's accident?

A. He rode a donkey.
B. He worked as a reporter.
C. He was in the hospital.
D. He went to college.

3   What happened next?

A. John went to Oregon.
B. John went back to college.
C. John won many awards.
D. John was on TV.

4   What happened after John left school?

A. He tried to get a job as a welder.
B. He went back to the hospital.
C. He went to the Middle East.
D. He was in an accident.

5   Where did John go in 1981?

A. The Middle East.
B. Washington, DC.
C. To college.
D. To Oregon.

6   Where did John study music?

A. The hospital.
B. Washington, DC.
C. The Middle East.
D. Oregon.

7   How did John travel in the Middle East?

A. By donkey.
B. He walked.
C. By car.
D. By airplane.

8   Why couldn't John call in his story in Oregon?

A. He didn't have a story.
B. He didn't have a quarter for the phone.
C. He forgot to make the call.
D. His wheelchair wouldn't fit in the phone booth.

9   When did John get his first TV job?

A. 1990
B. 1976
C. 1989
D. 1996

10   What did John do last?

A. He went to the Middle East.
B. He wrote a book.
C. He was in music school.
D. He was in Oregon.

Now use the Answer Key to check your answers. Mark the number you got correct on the Progress Chart.

UNIT 2
LESSON 7

VOCABULARY

unfortunately . . . something that can't be helped

directions . . . . . instructions about where to go

passengers . . . . . . people who ride in a car or plane

Read each passage. Then choose the correct answer for each question.

THE DESK

Ted wanted to make room for his new printer. He stacked papers on the floor and moved all the dirty dishes. He set a pile of files on his chair. Now his desk looked great. His office was a mess, though.

1 Ted's desk was—

    A. a mess
    B. covered with books
    C. cleaned up
    D. broken

2 Ted wanted to make room for—

    A. more dishes
    B. a printer
    C. more files
    D. his desk

LOOKING FOR FRANK

Ray and Terry were going to the airport to meet Frank. Unfortunately, they didn't know what he looked like. "How will we recognize him?" asked Terry.

They got to the airport late. They ran to the gate. All the passengers were gone except one. He held a small sign. It said, "HI! I'M FRANK."

3 Ray and Terry did not know—

    A. each other
    B. how to drive
    C. the airport
    D. Frank

4 Frank was holding—

    A. a sign
    B. his bag
    C. a ticket
    D. Terry's hand

THE FIRE STATION

Meg's class was visiting a fire station. Meg asked, "Do the firefighters really slide down this pole?"

    Suddenly, the fire alarm rang. The firefighters came flying down the pole. "I guess that answers my question," said Meg.

5 Meg and her class were visiting—

    A. a field
    B. a school
    C. a fire station
    D. a fire

6 The firefighters—

    A. slid down the pole
    B. were visiting Meg
    C. were not at the fire station
    D. were eating

LOST

Deb and her dad could not find Aunt Joan's house. "We've been on this block before,
Dad," said Deb. "Let's ask for directions." She asked a woman who was walking by.

    "Why, that address is right here," she said. There was Aunt Joan's house!

7 Deb and her dad were—

    A. coming home from Aunt Joan's
    B. circling the same block
    C. driving back home
    D. trying to get lost

8 Deb asked for—

    A. a soda
    B. a new car
    C. her dad
    D. directions

THE SHIRT

Rachel and Jack went shopping for a shirt for Jack. Rachel saw a shirt by the front door. "How about this one?" she asked.

    "Let's look around some more." Jack tried on dozens of shirts. They were about to walk out when Jack picked up the first shirt again. "This is perfect," he said.

9 Rachel and Jack were shopping—

    A. for a job
    B. for a shirt
    C. at home
    D. for a skirt

10 The shirt Jack chose was—

    A. by the front door
    B. at home
    C. in another store
    D. at his new job

Now use the Answer Key to check your answers. Mark the number you got correct on the Progress Chart.

LESSON 8

VOCABULARY

cooler . . . . . a holder for food
rustling . . . . a whispery sound
strengthen . . to get stronger

incline . . . . . . a steep hill
carribiners . . . hooks that attach ropes to a climbing belt

Read each passage. Then choose the correct answer for each question.

THE STRANGE NOISE

Jeff and Tim were going camping in a national park. There would be lots of bears. Tim bought a bear-proof cooler. They would keep their food in there so bears could not get at it.

That night they cooked up a great supper. Then they carefully cleaned up the campsite. They put all their food in the cooler. Then they got in their sleeping bags and went to sleep.

They both woke up to a strange noise. It was a rustling sound. Then they heard a POP, and then the sound of eating. The next morning, they saw what had happened. They had left the cooler open! The bear had a nice snack on all their food.

1 Jeff and Tim were going—

   A. fishing
   B. bear hunting
   C. hiking
   D. camping

2 The bear opened—

   A. the tent
   B. the sleeping bags
   C. the cooler
   D. the car

RIDING FOR HEALTH

Do you like horseback riding? It can be a challenging and rewarding sport. For some people, it is even more than that. Horseback riding helps them improve their health.

People in wheelchairs usually have a hard time sitting up on their own. A woman named Mira decided she wanted to try and strengthen her back muscles. She found a very gentle horse. With help, she was able to get up on the horse's back. At first, friends had to hold her up. But soon she could sit on the horse with no help. Horseback riding made a big difference in her life.

3 People in wheelchairs—

   A. sometimes have a hard time sitting up
   B. do not like to ride horses
   C. do not know how to get around
   D. cannot learn to sit up

4 Mira wanted to—

    A. own a horse
    B. strengthen her muscles
    C. quit using a wheelchair
    D. get a new wheelchair

7 Jess's vase was with—

    A. the masterpieces
    B. the first-grader's work
    C. the vases
    D. Cathy's bowl

THE POTTERY CLASS

Cathy and Jess decided to take a pottery class together. Jess was sure that she would be a great potter. Jess started building a vase. She would put flowers in it when she entertained friends. She started to build the walls. She kept adding more and more clay. Soon, the vase weighed ten pounds. When she was done, Jess sent it to be baked in the kiln.

When Jess came back the next week, she looked in the tray of pottery from her class. She saw Cathy's bowl, but no vase. Then she saw it. Someone had put her masterpiece in with the pottery made by the first-graders!

5 Jess wanted to make—

    A. a bowl
    B. a tray
    C. a vase
    D. flowers

6 Jess's vase weighed—

    A. ten pounds
    B. ten inches
    C. more than Cathy
    D. five pounds

THE BIG CLIMB

Lynn stood at the bottom of the big rock. It would be her first time trying to scale the steep incline to the very top. She had a pack with food, water, and a first-aid kit. Her belt jingled with ropes and carrabiners. She had special gloves and a light helmet. Her shoes were very tight. That was so her feet would not slip when she climbed. Lynn was well prepared for the climb.

8 Lynn had food in—

    A. her hands
    B. her belt
    C. her kit
    D. her pack

9 Lynn's shoes were—

    A. tight
    B. new
    C. ugly
    D. light

10 Lynn had special—

    A. ropes
    B. belt
    C. gloves
    D. feet

Now use the Answer Key to check your answers. Mark the number you got correct on the Progress Chart.

LESSON 9

VOCABULARY

barbecue . . . . . . cook over a fire
invitation . . . . . asking someone to come visit
specific . . . . very detailed

competition . . . . . a contest
instructor . . . . teacher
flexible . . . . can do many things

Read each passage. Then choose the correct answer for each question.

THANKSGIVING DINNER

Thanksgiving was coming in a few days. Laura and Jim decided to have a few friends for dinner. Jim would barbecue a turkey. Everyone else could bring a dish. Laura called all their friends, and everyone accepted the invitation. Everyone asked, "What should I bring?"

Laura said, "Oh, anything you like. Just surprise us!" On Thanksgiving day, their first guest arrived. He had cornbread. Jim put it on the table. Then the next friends appeared. They had cornbread, too!

"Uh-oh," said Jim. The next few guests arrived, and guess what they brought? You guessed it: cornbread! Next time, Laura will need to be a little more specific!

1 Laura told her guests to bring—

    A. a turkey
    B. a surprise
    C. cornbread
    D. a friend

2 Jim would barbecue—

    A. a dish
    B. a steak
    C. a turkey
    D. cornbread

3 Everyone brought—

    A. dishes
    B. guests
    C. turkeys
    D. cornbread

ICE SKATING

Ruth saw a figure skating competition on TV. The skaters zipped across the ice. They flipped and jumped through the air. Ruth got inspired. She went down and signed up for skating lessons. She went home dreaming of double toe flips and a sparkly outfit.

At her first lesson, Ruth's instructor said that first she needed to learn how to get up on skates. When she stood up on the ice, Ruth was surprised. One foot went one way and the other foot went the other way. She spent the whole time trying to stand up straight. By the end of the lesson, she knew that skating was harder than it looked!

4 Ruth signed up for—

    A. a skating competition
    B. swimming lessons
    C. a TV show
    D. skating lessons

5 Ruth wanted to—

    A. do toe flips
    B. fall down
    C. watch TV
    D. make an outfit

6 Ruth could not—

    A. be on TV
    B. take a lesson
    C. stand up on skates
    D. roller-skate

7 Clamshells protect—

    A. the sand
    B. the clam
    C. the birds
    D. the ocean

8 The clam's foot can—

    A. dig
    B. grow
    C. hide
    D. eat

9 The clam's neck—

    A. can dig
    B. can hide
    C. can eat
    D. gets water

10 A clamshell is hard to—

    A. hide
    B. open
    C. grow
    D. see

CLEVER CLAM

Have you seen clam shells on the beach? Clams are good at surviving in the ocean. The shell does a good job of protecting the clams. Clamshells are sealed very tight. You know this if you've ever tried to open an uncooked clam. The clam also has a foot. The foot is very flexible. It can change shape and do many things for the clam. It can dig the clam into the sand. This keeps the clams from getting picked up by birds. The clam has no head, but it has a neck. The neck can stick up out of the sand to take in water.

Now use the Answer Key to check your answers. Mark the number you got correct on the Progress Chart.

LESSON 10

VOCABULARY

barbed . . . . with sharp points
developed . . made
Australia . . . a country in the southern part of the world

diameter . . . . length across
Pueblo . . . . . an Indian village
ancestors . . . . family that lived in the past

Read each passage. Then choose the correct answer for each question.

BARBED WIRE

Have you ever been caught on a barbed wire fence? You can tear your clothes or get cut. Barbed wire is very hard to get through. The people who invented barbed wire wanted it that way.

Barbed wire was developed in the American West in 1850. People wanted a way of fencing their property. There weren't many trees, so they couldn't build wood fences. Wire fences were easy to knock over. A cow could just lean on the fence and it would tip over. People needed a new fencing material.

A man named Smith took a bit of cut wire. He wrapped it around a longer wire. The ends were sharp. If he put the sharp bits all along the wire, it made a good fence. Cattle and sheep would only try to get through barbed wire once. After that, they had learned their lesson.

1 Barbed wire can—

  A. go West
  B. tear your clothes

  C. get lost
  D. break easily

2 Barbed wire was invented in—

  A. 1850
  B. 1950
  C. 1860
  D. 1852

3 Barbed wire keeps cattle—

  A. very happy
  B. very busy
  C. in the West
  D. from getting out

THE BIG FIG

One of the biggest trees in the world is a fig tree in California. A thousand people could stand under it! It has been growing for over 130 years.

In 1874, the tree came to the United States on a ship from Australia. It was just a small sapling at the time. A sailor gave it to a little girl in California. She gave it to some friends.

In 1877, the tree was finally planted in the friends' yard. They made sure it got plenty of sun and water. The tree began to grow quickly. It grew and grew until it became enormous.

Today, the fig tree is 86 feet tall. It has a 16-foot diameter. The branches spread out more than 160 feet. It makes about 21,000 square feet of shade. That is about half the area of a football field!

4 The fig tree in California is—

A. one thousand years old
B. over 130 years old
C. over 86 years old
D. over 160 years old

5 The fig tree first came to America in—

A. 1874
B. 1877
C. 1970
D. 1974

6 The fig tree's shade covers half the area of—

A. a backyard
B. Australia
C. a football field
D. California

MARIA MARTINEZ

Maria Martinez was born in New Mexico in 1887. She lived in the Acoma Pueblo her entire life. When Maria was a child, she learned how to make pots. She used a special method that her ancestors had passed down for hundreds of years. As Maria got older, she became very good at making pottery. Soon, people from all over the world wanted her pots.

Maria always made her pots the same way. First she dug the clay up from the ground near her home. She would shape the clay with her hands. Then she would rub the pots with stones. That gave the pots a shiny surface. Often, she would paint designs on them. Then she baked them in a hot oven.

Maria taught her children to make pots in the old way. She died in 1980. Today, her family still makes the black, shiny pots.

7 Maria was born in—

A. 1980
B. 1887
C. 1890
D. 1987

8 Maria lived on—

A. a city
B. a big mountain
C. a ranch
D. the Acoma Pueblo

9 Maria shaped her pots—

A. with a machine
B. with a potter's wheel
C. with her hands
D. in a hot oven

10 Maria died in—

A. 1980
B. 1880
C. 1987
D. 1887

Now use the Answer Key to check your answers. Mark the number you got correct on the Progress Chart.

LESSON 11

VOCABULARY

environment . . the land
graze . . . . . . eat grass
hurdle . . . . . something you jump over

javelin . . . . a long pointed stick
excelled . . . . . . did very well
tournament . . . . a contest

Read each passage. Then choose the correct answer for each question.

OSTRICH BURGERS

Have you ever had an ostrich burger? Ostrich meat has less fat than beef. People have become interested in raising ostriches for food.

Australia has some ranches that raise ostriches. The big birds do well in the dry climate. Some places in the United States have the same kind of weather. Ostriches could probably do well in dry parts of the country.

Ostriches do not eat as much as cows. They have a little corn and grain, but not much grass. One cow can quickly eat all the grass in a big field. A rancher needs lots of land for the cattle to graze on. It would be easier to run an ostrich ranch. You would need much less land, and you would not have to spend as much money on food for the ostriches.

Another important difference is the ostrich's foot. Ostrich feet are wide and have soft pads on the bottom. They do not have sharp hooves like cows do. An ostrich's foot does not tear up the ground

when it walks. A cow's hoof tears up the ground when it walks. That keeps the grass from growing high. People have learned that cows are not good for the environment.

Maybe the meat of the future will be ostrich meat. You will see ostriches instead of cows when you drive in the country.

1 There are ostrich ranches in—

   A. the United States
   B. the country
   C. Australia
   D. the city

2 Ostriches eat—

   A. grass
   B. grain
   C. beef
   D. fields

3 Cows have to eat lots of—

   A. corn
   B. meat
   C. ostrich
   D. grass

4 Ostrich feet have—

    A. hooves
    B. soft pads
    C. grass
    D. toes

5 Ostrich meat has less—

    A. fat
    B. corn
    C. feet
    D. grass

THE FIRST SUPERSTAR

There are athletes who excel at several sports. They are called superstars. One of the first sports superstars was a woman named Babe Zaharias (say za•HA•ree•us).

Babe competed in track and field in the 1932 Olympics. She won gold medals for hurdle jumping, throwing the javelin, and the high jump. She broke a world record in the high jump. She won a medal in almost every race she entered.

After the Olympics, Babe moved on to other sports. She mastered tennis, bowling, and basketball. She competed in all of these sports. But there weren't many chances for a woman to play these sports. Babe wanted to find a sport that she could do all the time.

Babe went on to learn golf. Soon, she was one of the best female golfers ever. She won more than 30 contests in eight years. Babe kept competing no matter what. In 1953, she had cancer surgery. In 1954, she was back playing golf again. That year, Babe won the Women's National Open Tournament.

6 Babe was the first—

    A. female athlete
    B. female golfer
    C. superstar
    D. gold medalist

7 Babe won a gold medal in—

    A. jumping hurdles
    B. golfing
    C. basketball
    D. bowling

8 Babe broke a world record in—

    A. basketball
    B. bowling
    C. golf
    D. high jump

9 Babe was one of the best—

    A. female bowlers
    B. female golfers
    C. females artists
    D. female runners

10 In 1953, Babe had—

    A. a gold medal
    B. a golf tournament
    C. a high jump
    D. cancer surgery

Now use the Answer Key to check your answers. Mark the number you got correct on the Progress Chart.

LESSON 12

VOCABULARY

autumn . . . . the fall season
rivalry . . . . . a contest
emergency . . need for quick action

generator . . . something that makes power

Read the passage. It is about the San Francisco earthquake. Then choose the correct answer for each question.

OCTOBER 6, 1989

It was a warm autumn day in San Francisco, California. A big baseball game was about to start. It was the World Series. The San Francisco team was going to play a team from Oakland. The city of Oakland was just across the bay from San Francisco. The two teams had a big rivalry. Everyone was excited about the first game in the series. People from all over the country would be watching.

It was five o'clock in the afternoon. There were not many cars on the freeways. Lots of people had left work early to watch the big game. Some people stayed at their offices late. They wanted to avoid the traffic from the baseball game.

Suddenly, the ground began to shake. Buildings and trees started to sway back and forth. People knew right away what was happening. It was an earthquake! The shaking got harder and harder. Some buildings began to crack. Bricks and glass fell everywhere.

But that was only the beginning. The bridges that went to the city were swaying. One big bridge started to break apart. The roadway broke in half and cars went in the crack. People had to stop their cars and walk off the bridge.

A big freeway had two levels. The top level crashed down and many cars were stuck. Thirty people were killed on that freeway. It is lucky that there were not many cars on the road that day. More lives could have been lost.

In one part of San Francisco, a fire started. The fire spread quickly, and soon whole blocks of houses were gone. The city was in a state of emergency.

The power was out all over the Bay Area. People had to use flashlights or generators. Later that night the city was completely dark, except for the glow of burning buildings.

The baseball fans had run for their cars. It caused a big jam in the parking lot. The baseball players stood around. They did not know whether to go on with the game. The TV cameras had stopped working. People all over the country were looking at blank screens. Soon the news came on. "San Francisco Hit With a Huge Earthquake!" No one will ever forget that World Series game.

Identifying the Sequence

1 Which happened first?

  A. The baseball game started.
  B. The baseball game ended.
  C. The bridge broke apart.
  D. The earthquake started.

2 Which happened before the earthquake?

  A. The bridge fell down.
  B. People were watching the ball game.
  C. People rushed to their cars.
  D. Buildings started to sway.

3 What happened during the earthquake?

  A. People watched it on TV.
  B. The baseball game started.
  C. Bricks and glass fell.
  D. People used generators.

4 What happened after the earthquake?

  A. The ball game was back on TV.
  B. People drove home from work.
  C. Trees started to sway in the quake.
  D. Fire spread through a block of houses.

Identifying Details

5 The World Series game was being played in—

  A. San Francisco
  B. traffic
  C. Oakland
  D. on the bridge

6 The earthquake hit on—

  A. October 6, 1999
  B. October 9, 1989
  C. October 6, 1989
  D. October 8, 1989

7 The earthquake made one bridge—

  A. fall into the water
  B. break apart
  C. get bigger
  D. take more cars

8 On that bridge, people had to—

  A. drive off
  B. jump off
  C. walk off
  D. stay put

9 After the fire started—

  A. it spread to lots of houses
  B. it went out very quickly
  C. the bridge burned down
  D. the ball game started

10 That night, people had to—

  A. go to work
  B. fix the bridge
  C. use generators
  D. shake the ground

Now use the Answer Key to check your answers. Mark the number you got correct on the Progress Chart.

UNIT 3
LESSON 13

VOCABULARY

coax . . . . . to get someone to do something

monitor . . . . a computer screen

veteran . . . . . someone who has a lot of experience

Read each passage. Then choose the correct answer for each question.

"Paintbrush is up a tree," said Liz.

"Oh, no," cried Jamie, "Not again!" The girls tried everything to coax Paintbrush down. Finally, Jamie's dad climbed up the tree with a pillowcase. He threw the pillowcase over the cat. Paintbrush was saved!

1 What is the main idea?

   A. Paintbrush is not a good cat.
   B. Paintbrush is always up a tree.
   C. Paintbrush wants to live in the tree.
   D. Jamie is getting tired of her cat.

2 What would be the best title?

   A. Stuck Again
   B. How to Climb a Tree
   C. Paintbrush the Cat
   D. Dad Climbs a Tree

Gabe was visiting his friend Matt. "What do you want to do today?" asked Matt.

"Anything is fine with me," said Gabe.

"How about the museum?" said Matt.

"I don't like museums," said Gabe.

"How about the street festival?"

"I don't like crowds."

"What do you like to do?" asked Matt.

"Oh, I'm easy to please!"

3 What is the main idea?

   A. Gabe is easy to please.
   B. Matt doesn't have good ideas.
   C. Gabe is not easy to please.
   D. Gabe and Matt are not friends.

4 What would be the best title?

   A. Gabe and Matt
   B. The Picky Guest
   C. The Street Festival
   D. Matt and the Museum

Marta went to see Jeff's new computer. She looked around but she didn't see a computer monitor anywhere.

When Jeff arrived, Marta said, "I don't see a computer!" Jeff pulled out a small case from his backpack.

He had a computer that fit in his hand!

5 What is the main idea?

   A. Marta has never seen a computer.
   B. Jeff was trying to trick Marta.
   C. Marta was surprised by Jeff's new computer.
   D. Marta and Jeff are not good friends.

6 What would be the best title?

   A. A Tricky Friend
   B. A Nosy Friend
   C. Jeff's Room
   D. Jeff's New Computer

Jamal had only been running for two months. Most of these guys in the race were veteran runners. Jamal was nervous.

The runners took off. Before he knew it, Jamal crossed the finish line. He had won the race!

7 What is the main idea?

   A. Jamal was not a good runner.
   B. The race was very hard.
   C. The race was not too hard.
   D. Jamal was a better runner than he thought.

8 What would be the best title?

   A. How to Run a Race
   B. Jamal's Surprise Race
   C. Jamal is Nervous
   D. How to Lose a Race

Gail and Jean came to some trash on the hiking trail. Gail put it in her pack. A little further on, Gail picked up more trash. By the end of the hike, Gail's pack was full of trash, but the trail looked much better.

9 What is the main idea?

   A. Gail is a good hiker.
   B. Gail and Jean got lost.
   C. Gail helped keep the trail clean.
   D. Gail got tired of picking up trash.

10 What would be the best title?

   A. Taking Care of the Trail
   B. A Good Hiker
   C. A Long Hike
   D. Gail and Jean

Now use the Answer Key to check your answers. Mark the number you got correct on the Progress Chart.

UNIT 3
LESSON 14
VOCABULARY

basement . . . space under a house
versatile . . . has many uses

barren . . . . . things cannot grow
nourished . . . . fed

Read each passage. Then choose the correct answer for each question.

Mike and his family were looking at new houses. Some had big backyards. Some had neat staircases. Some had big basements where Mike could set up his trains. One house had all of these things. It was perfect!

On the way out, Mike saw a beautiful bicycle. The man said it had belonged to his son. Now his son was grown up. Mike said the bike was great.

When Mike's family bought the house, there was an extra surprise.

The man gave Mike his son's old bike!

1 What is the main idea?

A. Mike and his family saw a lot of great houses.
B. Mike's perfect house had a special surprise.
C. Mike wanted the old bike.
D. Mike's family couldn't find a house.

2 What would be the best title?

A. Looking for Houses
B. The Old Bicycle
C. Mike's Perfect House
D. Mike and His Family

Have you ever seen bamboo? It grows very straight. It can grow very tall and thick like a tree. But bamboo is really giant grass. It grows very fast. Some bamboo can grow three feet a day! Bamboo is hollow and light. But it is also very strong. You can bend it to make things. There are bamboo fences, boats, and furniture. Young bamboo is very tender. People cook it in vegetable dishes. Bamboo has many uses. It is very versatile.

3 What is the main idea?

A. Bamboo is very strong.
B. Bamboo is good to eat.
C. Bamboo is a type of tree.
D. Bamboo has many uses.

4 What would be the best title?

A. How to Make Furniture
B. How to Cook Bamboo
C. The Useful Plant
D. Growing a Bamboo Tree

Long ago, the island of Greece had large forests. The Greek people wanted to explore the oceans. They cut down many trees to build boats.

At first, the Greek farmers were happy. They had more land for their crops. But soon the rain started to wash away the dirt. They lost a lot of good topsoil. Then farmers cut down more trees. They wanted to grow olive trees. Soon, no other trees could grow in Greece. Many parts of the land became barren.

5 What is the main idea?

A. The Greek people built boats.
B. Cutting trees was bad for the soil.
C. The Greek farmers were very happy.
D. The Greek people like olive trees.

6 What is the main idea of the first paragraph?

A. The Greek people wanted to explore.
B. The Greek people cut trees to build boats.
C. The Greek people liked forests.
D. The Greek people did not like trees.

7 What would be the best title?

A. Olive Trees in Greece
B. Greek Boats
C. The Lost Forests of Greece
D. Farming in Greece

Some plants do not need dirt to live. They only need air! Moss and lichens can grow on rocks. They can even grow on buildings. They are nourished by the air around them. They get water and food from the mist and rain.

Other plants can live without soil. But they have to grow on another plant. They take their food and water from it. Mistletoe is an air plant that lives in trees. A tree can die if the mistletoe takes away too much food and water.

8 What is the main idea?

A. Some plants grow on buildings.
B. Most plants need soil.
C. Mistletoe is bad for trees.
D. Some plants can live on air.

9 What is the main idea of the first paragraph?

A. All plants can live on rocks.
B. Some plants can live on rocks or buildings.
C. Most plants do not need soil.
D. All plants can live on air.

10 What would be the best title?

A. Living on Air
B. Mistletoe
C. Moss and Lichen
D. How to Grow Trees

Now use the Answer Key to check your answers. Mark the number you got correct on the Progress Chart.

LESSON 15

VOCABULARY

architect ... someone who designs buildings

jot .... draw or write quickly

substitute .... taking the place of someone else

explode ..... pop open loudly

Read each passage. Then choose the correct answer for each question.

Did you ever have an idea just pop into your head? It often happens when you're thinking of something else. Some of the best ideas come that way.

That happened to a man named John Lloyd Wright. He was the son of the architect Frank Lloyd Wright. John was an architect, too. He was making plans for a new building. Suddenly, he got a great idea for a toy. He was too busy to work on the idea. But he did jot down a sketch on a paper napkin. Later he worked on his new toy idea. The toy was a big success. It was a building kit. It was called "Lincoln Logs."

1 What is the main idea?

A. Some good ideas come when you don't expect it.
B. It is very hard to come up with ideas for new toys.
C. You have to be very smart to have a good idea.
D. Lincoln Logs are a very popular toy.

2 What is the main idea of the first paragraph?

A. Most people don't have any good ideas.
B. Sometimes ideas just pop into your head.
C. You have to think hard to have a good idea.
D. It is easy to forget good ideas.

3 What would be the best title?

A. Lincoln Logs
B. Frank Lloyd Wright
C. Good Idea!
D. Becoming an Architect

Most people like popcorn. It is fun to watch the dried corn explode. It is even more fun to eat! Lots of people put butter or melted cheese on popcorn.

Did you ever think about how popcorn was discovered? We know that American Indians were the first to grow corn. They shared it with European settlers. They also showed them how to make popcorn.

No one really knows when they discovered that old corn would pop. Maybe someone set a bowl of dried corn by the fire. If it sat too long, they would have had a big surprise!

4 What is the main idea?

    A. Popcorn is a good snack.
    B. Popcorn is good with butter or cheese.
    C. No one knows how popcorn was discovered.
    D. You make popcorn with dried corn.

5 What is the main idea of the first paragraph?

    A. Popcorn is not good for you.
    B. Popcorn is an unusual snack.
    C. Popcorn is good with butter.
    D. Popcorn is fun to eat.

6 What would be the best title?

    A. How Popcorn Pops
    B. Who Discovered Popcorn?
    C. How to Make Popcorn
    D. The American Indians

Maria stood in front of the goalpost. She was the substitute goalie for her team. She had only been on the team for a month. Maria and her family had just moved to America from Italy. She did not know much English, but she did know soccer.

This was the first time Maria had been in a game. She knew she could do it, but she was very nervous. The score was tied.

Her team was struggling to defend the goal. Suddenly, the ball was heading right for Maria! She dove and caught the ball. Her teammates cheered for the new goalie.

7 What is the main idea?

    A. Maria did well in her first American soccer game.
    B. Maria could not play soccer well.
    C. Maria did not like to play soccer.
    D. Maria did not like being in America.

8 What is the main idea of the first paragraph?

    A. Maria did not like American soccer.
    B. Maria was new to American soccer.
    C. Maria didn't know if she could play.
    D. The team did not want Maria to play.

9 What is the main idea of the last paragraph?

    A. Maria's team did not play well.
    B. Maria saw the ball heading for the goal.
    C. Maria caught the ball and saved her team.
    D. Maria's team didn't think she could play.

10 What would be the best title?

    A. American Soccer
    B. Soccer in Italy
    C. Maria in Italy
    D. Maria's Big Save

Now use the Answer Key to check your answers. Mark the number you got correct on the Progress Chart.

LESSON 16

VOCABULARY

architecture . . . the planning of buildings

traditional . . . . used in the past

issue . . . . a problem to discuss

Read each passage. Then choose the correct answer for each question.

Julia Morgan always loved to build things. When she went to college, her teachers encouraged her to go to architecture school in Paris. Julia tried, but the school would not let her in. They didn't understand why a woman would want to build things. But soon they did let Julia into the school and she began a promising career.

After the 1906 earthquake in San Francisco, Julia helped rebuild the city. She built a famous house for William Randolph Hearst. There is a movie about it called *Citizen Kane.*

Julia Morgan worked as an architect for over 50 years. She was always a quiet, modest woman. But her buildings tell the story of her great talent.

1 What is the main idea?

  A. Julia Morgan built the house in *Citizen Kane.*
  B. Julia Morgan built San Francisco.
  C. Julia Morgan was a great architect.
  D. Julia Morgan built lots of houses.

2 What is the main idea of the first paragraph?

  A. Julia always wanted to go to Paris.
  B. Julia always like to build things.
  C. Julia was an unusual child.
  D. Julia did not like architecture.

3 What would be the best title?

  A. Julia Morgan
  B. Architecture
  C. The 1906 Earthquake
  D. Citizen Kane

The first surfers were Hawaiian sailors who had to get to shore. They learned to steer their little boats over the waves. Soon they were riding the waves on large boards.

Surfing became popular in the 1940s, when Hawaii became part of the United States. By 1968, surfing was popular all over the world.

Today people surf on traditional big boards. But now there are smaller boards called boogie boards. Some people even ride the waves without a board. This is called body surfing.

4 What is the main idea?

A. Surfing is a hard sport to do.
B. Surfing is too dangerous.
C. Surfing is popular everywhere.
D. Surfing began in Hawaii.

5 What is the main idea of the first paragraph?

A. The first sailors were surfers.
B. The first surfer couldn't swim.
C. Sailors in Hawaii had small boats.
D. Surfing started in Hawaii.

6 What would be the best title?

A. Body Surfing
B. Surf's Up!
C. Boogie Boarding
D. How to Surf

Coyotes have always lived in the desert. Often there is not much to eat. The coyotes have always had to struggle to get along.

Recently, people have built houses in the desert. Some have put in swimming pools. This is great for the coyotes. They have a place to drink. They can check out the garbage can for food.

In some desert cities, coyotes walk down streets and through traffic. It is not safe for the coyotes. They can get hit by cars. People also do not like finding coyotes in their backyards.

It is a tough issue. On the one hand,

coyotes are true pests. They can carry disease. But it is people who have invaded the coyotes' home, not the other way around!

7 What is the main idea?

A. Coyotes cause problems in desert cities.
B. Coyotes should move from desert cities.
C. People have never liked coyotes.
D. People should be nicer to coyotes.

8 What is the main idea of the first paragraph?

A. Coyotes have always lived in cities.
B. Coyotes have moved into the city.
C. Most cities have coyotes.
D. Coyotes have a hard time surviving in the desert.

9 What is the main idea of the last paragraph?

A. People have moved away from coyotes.
B. Coyotes are a dangers to pets.
C. People have moved into the coyotes' home.
D. Coyotes are true pests.

10 What would be the best title?

A. A True Pest
B. Desert Cities
C. Coyotes and Pets
D. Coyotes in the City

Now use the Answer Key to check your answers. Mark the number you got correct on the Progress Chart.

LESSON 17

VOCABULARY

protective . . . something that protects
biology . . . . study of the human body
astronomy . . study of the stars
geology . . . . study of the earth

philosophy . . . . the study of how people think
engineering . . . . planned construction

Read each passage. Then choose the correct answer for each question.

It is inspiring to study nature. Plants and animals work together like a well-made machine. Human inventors often can get ideas from watching nature.

For example, turtles have a protective shell. It is made of bony plates. Turtles can pull in their heads and feet for safety. The same idea was used to make a tank. It has a hard shell that protects the people inside. Turtles can't move very fast, and neither can tanks. But at least everyone stays safe!

Now look up at the sky. Carefully watch how the bird flies. The bird's wings are curved on top. The bottoms of the wings are flat. This helps lift the bird up into the sky. Airplanes use the same idea for their wing design.

Animals and birds are very good at keeping warm. Most birds have feathers that keep in their body heat. People will sometimes stuff their coats or blankets with feathers. The feathers trap warm air near the body. That way, they can stay nice and warm no matter how cold it is.

1 What is the main idea?

A. Humans get lots of good ideas from nature.
B. Humans do not like to study nature.
C. Nature is not a good thing to study.
D. Humans get all their ideas from books.

2 What is the main idea of the first paragraph?

A. Nature has lots of dangerous ideas.
B. Humans thought up machines.
C. Nature is very inspiring to study.
D. Humans make a lot of mistakes.

3 What is the main idea of the last paragraph?

A. Birds show us a good way to keep warm.
B. Birds are not very bright.
C. People do not like most birds.
D. Birds are smarter than people.

4 Which sentence tells the main idea?

A. Turtles do not move very fast.
B. Airplanes are designed like birds.

C. Inventors get ideas from nature.

D. People can use bird feathers to keep warm.

5 What would be the best title?

A. Nature's Machine

B. Nature's Models

C. Human Inventors

D. Feather Coats

Most people have heard of Leonardo Da Vinci (say da•VIN•chee). His most famous painting is called Mona Lisa. It is a picture of a young woman. The painting isn't even finished. The edges of the painting were not filled in. But the Mona Lisa is still considered the greatest painting ever made. Da Vinci would often start beautiful pieces of art. Then he would get bored and move on to the next project.

Da Vinci was interested in almost everything. He studied science, engineering, painting, sculpture, music, math, and biology. Da Vinci did more than read books. He made plans for inventions.

Some of Da Vinci's inventions were the parachute, submarines, and swimming fins. He drew plans for making a compass, a chainsaw, and even contact lenses! He usually did not make these inventions. But his plans have been used by inventors for hundreds of years.

Da Vinci is the greatest inventor of all time. Every day we see his inventions. People will always remember the name Da Vinci.

6 What is the main idea?

A. Da Vinci got bored easily.

B. Da Vinci was a great artist and inventor.

C. Da Vinci invented bridges and canals.

D. DaVinci was not a very good artist.

7 What is the main idea of the first paragraph?

A. Da Vinci was a good inventor.

B. Da Vinci did not like to paint.

C. Da Vinci is not well known.

D. Mona Lisa is the greatest painting ever.

8 What is the main idea of the second paragraph?

A. Da Vinci was a scientist.

B. Da Vinci got bored with painting.

C. Da Vinci forgot to finish things.

D. Da Vinci was interested in many subjects.

9 Which sentence tells the main idea?

A. Da Vinci was the greatest inventor of all time.

B. Da Vinci is not well known today.

C. People still like Da Vinci's paintings.

D. Da Vinci would often get bored.

10 What would be the best title?

A. A Great Painter

B. The Mona Lisa

C. The World's Greatest Inventor

D. How to Invent Things

Now use the Answer Key to check your answers. Mark the number you got correct on the Progress Chart.

LESSON 18

VOCABULARY

horizon . . . . the place where sky and ground meet

inky . . . . . . very dark

antennae . . . . thin feelers

hastened . . . . hurried; speeded up

Read the passage. It tells the story of The Time Machine *by H.G. Wells. The story is about a man who travels to the future. Then choose the correct answer for each question.*

I stopped the Time Machine and looked around me. The sky was not blue, but mostly an inky black. Off to the west there was a bit of red. The sun lay low on the horizon. It looked like a huge red hump.

The machine had stopped on a beach. The sea was very still. There was no wind, and so there were no waves. The water rose and fell. It was as if the sea were breathing.

Quite near to me there was a crab. It was as big as a table. It moved slowly towards me, with claws swaying. Its antennas waved like thin whips.

Suddenly, I felt a sting on my cheeks. I reached up, and felt something like thread. I turned, and there was another crab. Its claws were opened to snap at me.

I moved forward a hundred years. Little had changed on the beach. The sky was black and red, and the sea was still smooth. The crabs still roamed the beach. So I traveled on. I moved ahead quickly, on to thousands of years in the future. After thirty million years had passed, I stopped again.

The red sun now filled the sky. The crabs were gone. The beach was dusted with snow and it was bitter cold. Ice floated on the blood-red sea.

Nothing moved on the earth or in the sky. The sea only made a rippling whisper. That was the only sound to be heard. All the sounds of the world were gone.

I felt sick at this sight. I got off the machine. As I stood there, I suddenly saw movement. A strange creature came hopping up the beach. It had no arms or legs. It was shaped like a football. All at once, I had seen enough of the future. I hastened back to my machine.

As I traveled back in time, the sun became golden again. Once more, the sky was blue. The land changed, and I started to see evidence of people. I was glad to be safe from the future. At last, the walls of my own house were around me. I saw my room, my tools, and my books. They were just as I left them.

Identifying the Sequence

1 The first time, how far did the time machine travel?

   A. One hundred years into the past.
   B. One hundred years into the future.
   C. Thirty million years into the future.
   D. One month into the future.

2 The second time, how far did the time machine travel?

   A. Thirty million years into the future.
   B. One hundred years into the future.
   C. One month into the future.
   D. One hundred years into the past.

3 Where was the last place the Time Machine traveled?

   A. Thirty million years in the future.
   B. One month into the future.
   C. One hundred years into the past.
   D. To the present.

Identifying Details

4 The crabs were—

   A. In the sky.
   B. In the past.
   C. On the beach.
   D. in the sea.

5 30 million years in the future—

   A. The sun was golden.
   B. The sun filled the sky.
   C. The sun was a red lump.
   D. The sun was gone.

6 The crabs were—

   A. As big as the beach.
   B. As small as a dime.
   C. As big as a table.
   D. A normal size.

Understanding the Main Idea

7 What is the main idea?

   A. The past is better than the future.
   B. The future could be scary.
   C. Time travel is a lot of fun.
   D. The future is better that the past.

8 What is the main idea of the last paragraph?

   A. It was good to get back to the present.
   B. He wanted to keep going into the future.
   C. He wanted to travel into the past.
   D. He did not like his house.

9 Which sentence tells the main idea?

   A. Nothing moved on the earth or in the sky.
   B. It was as if the sea were breathing.
   C. The red sun now filled the sky.
   D. I was glad to be safe from the future.

10 What would be the best title?

   A. Fighting Giant Crabs
   B. How to Use a Time Machine
   C. A Journey Through Time
   D. My Life on the Beach

Now use the Answer Key to check your answers. Mark the number you got correct on the Progress Chart.

UNIT 4
LESSON 19

VOCABULARY

scent . . . . . smell
fragrance . . a nice smell

cobbler . . . . . a dessert with fruit
screeching . . . a harsh, loud sound

Read each passage. Then choose the correct word to fill in the blank.

NIGHT BLOOMERS

Some flowers start blooming only after the (1)_____ goes down. They are called night bloomers. Often they have a wonderful scent. They fill the air with fragrance until (2)_____. But when the sun comes up, they close up. They don't reopen until nighttime.

1　A. sun　　　　C. cloud
　　B. flower　　　D. bugs

2　A. flowers　　C. lunchtime
　　B. night　　　D. morning

FOUND

Jazz the dog decided to go exploring. She smelled something interesting. She just followed her nose. She (3)_____ a long way. Soon it was night. Jazz looked around. She was in a strange neighborhood. Jazz was definitely (4)_____. Then she saw a headlight coming toward her. She was ready to run, but then she saw that it was Jim. He had been looking for her.

3　A. flew　　　　C. skated
　　B. walked　　　D. sat

4 A. lost C. funny
    B. bored D. fun

THE ORCHARD

A big (5)_____ hit the farm. The wind blew and blew the trees in the orchard. It blew hard against Marta's peach trees. Soon, the peaches started to fall off. When the storm was over, Marta and Kit went outside and looked around. Marta was very disappointed. All of her (6)_____ were on the ground. Kit said, "It's okay, Marta. We'll make a lot of peach jam and cobbler!"

5 A. party C. storm
    B. field D. peach

6 A. peaches C. trees
    B. friends D. farm

DEER

Have you ever heard a deer make noise? Most people think of them as silent creatures. It's true that deer seldom make (7)_____. They do not "talk" to each other. But when it needs to, a deer can make a screeching sound. It sounds a little like a (8)_____.

7 A. food C. scared
    B. noise D. run

8 A. smile C. scream
    B. foot D. smile

THE PLAY

Larry and Greg's plans were ruined. They were going to go on a big hike today, but it was raining. They sat in the attic, staring out the window. "What are we going to do now?" asked Greg. "I'm bored."

    Larry looked in a closet. "Look at this stuff," he said. "I know what we can do." The (9)_____ had lots of costumes. Larry picked out a pirate outfit. Greg found a parrot (10)_____. They made up a funny play.

9 A. rain C. closet
    B. hike D. attic

10 A. movie C. storm
    B. costume D. attic

Now use the Answer Key to check your answers. Mark the number you got correct on the Progress Chart.

LESSON 20

VOCABULARY

bloated . . . . filled too full
antique . . . something very old

cautious . . . . . very careful
damage . . . . . to hurt

Read each passage. Then choose the correct word to fill in the blank.

WAKE UP!

Every night it's the same thing. Rachel sits up late at her computer. She always finds interesting things to do on the Internet. For hours she goes from site to site. Often she does not notice how the time goes by.

One morning, Rachel's mom looked in her bedroom. Rachel had fallen asleep at the computer! She had some funny marks on her (1)_____. They came from using the (2)_____ as a pillow!

Look back at the passage. Choose the correct word to fill in the blank.

1 A. face   C. tickle
   B. foot   D. computer

2 A. bed   C. face
   B. sleep   D. keyboard

THE HUNGRY DOG

Richard got a new dog named Golda. Golda liked to eat a bit too much. She would eat her breakfast. Then she would try to eat Richard's breakfast, too. She would beg for a snack all day. When dinnertime came, Golda would gobble down her (3)_____ as if she had been starved all day.

One day, Richard had left out some brownies. When he got home, the brownie (4)_____ was empty! All that was left was one brownie with a dog's paw print on it. Golda was sitting on the kitchen floor, looking a little bloated!

Look back at the passage. Choose the correct word to fill in the blank.

3 A. breakfast   C. dinner
   B. snack   D. dog

4 A. plate   C. breakfast
   B. dog   D. dinner

THE HOME MOVIE

Miguel and his little sister, Lisa, were watching home movies. A birthday party came on the screen. A little boy sat in front of the cake clapping his hands.

"Who is that?" asked Lisa.

"That's me when I was little," said Miguel. "that was my first birthday (5)_____."

"I never had a birthday party like that," said Lisa. "It's not fair!"

"Yes you did. You just don't remember," said Miguel. Just then, another birthday party flashed on the (6)_____. This was a big party for a happy little girl.

"That's (7)_____!" cried Lisa. "What a great party!"

Look back at the passage. Choose the correct word to fill in the blank.

5 A. party   C. sister
   B. movie   D. clapping

6 A. movie   C. screen
   B. picture   D. sister

7 A. cake   C. baby
   B. Grandma   D. me

THE ANTIQUE CAR

Heather took Shane's antique car to the car wash. She drove there very cautiously. She did not want to damage Shane's (8)_____.

When Heather got to the car wash, she paid her (9)_____. She got the car in the right place. She drove it into the washing machine.

Suddenly, Heather looked in the back seat. The window was open a crack! The (10)_____ was spraying on the back seat. It took her all afternoon to get the water mopped up.

Look back at the passage. Choose the correct word to fill in the blank.

8 A. pet   C. cat
   B. car   D. water

9 A. money   C. car
   B. water   D. machine

10 A. sun   C. mop
   B. water   D. car

Now use the Answer Key to check your answers. Mark the number you got correct on the Progress Chart.

LESSON 21

VOCABULARY

product . . . . something that is made
endangered . in trouble
humor . . . . being funny

lasso . . . . . . a rope with a loop at the end
champion . . . . winner

Read each passage. Then choose the correct word to fill in the blank.

GET PRETTY AND SAVE THE EARTH

There are stores that sell all sorts of special bath products. They have soaps and lotions and makeup. What is so special about soap or makeup? These are made with endangered plants and flowers. These products could help save the planet.

It started when a woman named Liz Phair was reading about the rainforest in South America. She read that it was being burned down. She knew that the (1)_____ helped keep the earth cool.

So Liz did some research. She found plants and flowers that grow only in the rainforest. She used them to make (2)_____ and lotion. The products became very popular. Liz ordered more flowers and plants from the rainforest. She hoped it would keep countries from (3)_____ it down. Liz Phair's soaps and lotions have helped educate people about the rainforest.

Look back at the passage. Choose the correct word to fill in the blank.

1. A. earth   C. soap
   B. rainforest   D. plants

2. A. soaps   C. plants
   B. flowers   D. bath

3. A. looking   C. burning
   B. taste   D. rainforest

WILL RODGERS

Rodeos are shows with cowboys, horses, and bulls. Rodeos were once very popular. The cowboys rode the horses or tried to catch the bulls. One of the most famous rodeo cowboys ever was named Will Rodgers. He was a Cherokee Indian. He lived in the early 1900s. Will always worked with horses. He would rope (4)_____ that tried to run away. That is called lassoing. Will liked to practice lassoing all the time. He would (5)_____ animals. Sometimes he would even lasso people, but only for a joke.

Will liked to make people laugh. Soon he was telling jokes in shows. He became famous for his (6)_____. He also was in movies and wrote for the newspaper. Will Rodgers became America's favorite cowboy.

Look back at the passage. Choose the correct word to fill in the blank.

4 A. rodeos   C. chase
   B. horses   D. lasso

5 A. rodeo   C. lasso
   B. chase   D. joke

6 A. humor   C. cowboys
   B. rodeo   D. steers

THE TREE CLIMBING CHAMPS

Lynn and her friend, Liz, were heading to the tree-climbing contest. They were both a little nervous. It was the first time they had ever entered the contest. They knew it would be a stiff competition. Only men had ever been the tree-climbing champions. But Lynn and Liz knew they were good tree-climbers. They had been trained by one of the best (7)_____ in the state.

The women were all set to go. They had their (8)_____ set up just right. They gave each other a wave for good luck. Then they heard the signal. Off they went, as (9)_____ as they could. It was a close race, but there were two winners. Lynn and Liz were the new (10)_____!

Look back at the passage. Choose the correct word to fill in the blank.

7 A. swimmers   C. tree
   B. friends   D. climbers

8 A. nervous   C. ropes
   B. winners   D. cars

9 A. cold   C. rope
   B. fast   D. tree

10 A. climbers   C. race
   B. friends   D. champions

Now use the Answer Key to check your answers. Mark the number you got correct on the Progress Chart.

LESSON 22

VOCABULARY

creatures . . . living things
theory . . . . . idea
meteor . . . . a rock from outer space
rumor . . . . . unproved news

Canada . . . . . a country north of the
United States
sturdy . . . . . . strong

Read each passage. Then choose the correct word to fill in the blank.

THE DINOSAURS

You have probably read about dinosaurs. They lived on earth a long time ago. We know what these creatures looked like. Some were very big. Some had wings. Many could swim. Some of them ate (1)_____. Others ate only vegetables.

Then the dinosaurs died off. That is the part we do not know about. Why did they disappear? One theory is that sickness killed the dinosaurs. Some think that other animals ate the dinosaurs' eggs. Then (2)_____ dinosaurs could not be born.

We know the weather changed at that time. One idea is that a meteor hit earth. That made big clouds of dust. The dust blocked the sun for many years. It got very (3)_____ and ice covered everything. The dinosaurs could not survive.

No one really knows for sure what happened to the dinosaurs. What do you think?

Look back at the passage. Choose the correct word to fill in the blank.

1   A. water   C. ice
    B. meat   D. food

2   A. baby   C. swimming
    B. big   D. egg

3   A. hot   C. red
    B. cold   D. clean

THE LONG JOURNEY

It was a freezing day in Alaska. Jane was standing in a long line. Most of the people in the line were men. They were waiting to cross over the border to Canada. There was a rumor that gold had been found at Dawson's Creek. That was why all the (4)_____ were there. They were getting ready to climb a steep mountain. Everyone had to bring food and other gear along. Otherwise they would not be let into Canada.

Jane had all her supplies ready to go. But how would she get everything up the (5)_____? Some men in the line had carts or sleds. Some hauled their gear up the hill on their backs. Jane knew she could not do this alone. Suddenly, she saw a few other woman off to the side. They had their food and gear stacked beside them. They also had a sled. Jane offered to help them pull their sled. They put part of the gear on the (6)_____. They made three trips up the mountain. It helped to work together.

Look back at the passage. Choose the correct word to fill in the blank.

4 A. snow   C. people
   B. gear   D. gold

5 A. sled   C. mountain
   B. line   D. Canada

6 A. mountain   C. trip
   B. stories   D. sled

A BRIGHT IDEA

What would we do without lightbulbs? They are a great invention. But most lightbulbs do not last long. Some last for a few months. Some only (7)_____ for a few weeks! Most lightbulbs have to be replaced many times.

Why do they stop working? It is because of the material inside. There are tiny wires (8)_____ the glass. They can break easily. Then you have to throw the bulb away.

Someone made a type of lightbulb that lasted much longer than the average bulb. It also produced a very bright light. Unfortunately, the (9)_____ burned hotter, too. Sometimes the light would catch drapes or shades on fire. That bulb was not such a bright idea!

Today, there are some new kinds of lightbulbs. One kind is made of stronger stuff. It does not (10)_____ so quickly. You can get lightbulbs that will last for two years. They are more expensive, but it might be worth it if you don't like to change lightbulbs.

Look back at the passage. Choose the correct word to fill in the blank.

7 A. break   C. walk
   B. work   D. stop

8 A. inside   C. outside
   B. under   D. through

9 A. day   C. bright
   B. night   D. bulb

10 A. light   C. break
   B. wish   D. open

Now use the Answer Key to check your answers. Mark the number you got correct on the Progress Chart.

LESSON 23

VOCABULARY

inspired . . . . gave the idea for
landscape . . . a place in nature
sculpture . . . . an art piece that is made out of clay

rarely . . . . not often
populated . . . . has lots of people
sightings . . . . . to see something

Read each passage. Then choose the correct answer for each question.

SEEING WITH HER HANDS

Georgia O'Keefe was a world-famous artist. Her paintings have been seen by people all over the world. She is known for pictures of gigantic flowers and animal skulls floating in the air. Some paintings are very simple. They are just made up of lines and circles and other shapes. O'Keefe could always tell a story with her (1)_____.

Toward the end of her life, O'Keefe lived alone in New Mexico. She loved the landscape of the mountains. They inspired many beautiful paintings. As O'Keefe grew older, her eyesight got worse. Finally she became completely (2)_____. O'Keefe got helpers to live with her. But she was still very sad. She could not see to make her (3)_____ anymore.

One day, a young man came to visit her. He was a sculptor. He admired O'Keefe's paintings. She told him sadly that she did not paint anymore. The young (4)_____ said, "I can help you see with your hands." He taught her to make

sculptures. Soon O'Keefe was making large, round pieces. They are very graceful looking. O'Keefe had a new way to express herself. She made (5)_____ until the day she died. She was 99 years old.

Look back at the passage. Choose the correct word to fill in the blank.

1 A. mountains   C. animals
   B. paintings   D. flowers

2 A. older   C. sad
   B. lost   D. blind

3 A. animals   C. paintings
   B. sculptures   D. mountains

4 A. painting   C. sculpture
   B. mountain   D. man

5 A. sculptures   C. animals
   B. mountains   D. paintings

THE MYSTERY OF LOCH NESS

In Scotland there is a legend. It is about a strange creature. It looks a little like a big fish. But it also looks like a dragon. It lives in a huge lake, but rarely comes to the surface. They call it the Loch Ness Monster.

Many people claimed to have seen the monster, but there is only one photo of it. It does look like a (6)_____. It has a very long neck and tail. Some people doubt that the photograph is real. They think someone made it up. People question why there are no other pictures of the creature. They say the (7)_____ of the Loch Ness Monster is a folktale.

Loch Ness is a very big lake. It is also very deep. There are many places a creature could hide. People argue that the Loch Ness monster could be afraid of (8)_____. It may want to stay away from areas that are populated.

Many, many people have claimed to have seen the (9)_____. Over the years, there have been hundreds of sightings. People even have a nickname for the Loch Ness monster. They call it "Nessy." People in (10)_____ are proud of their mysterious beast.

Look back at the passage. Choose the correct word to fill in the blank.

6 A. wings   C. heads
   B. dragon   D. lake

7 A. lake   C. creature
   B. story   D. beast

8 A. lake   C. people
   B. water   D. dragons

9 A. creature   C. lake
   B. stories   D. Scotland

10 A. lakes   C. Scotland
   B. places   D. folktales

Now use the Answer Key to check your answers. Mark the number you got correct on the Progress Chart.

LESSON 24

VOCABULARY

achievements .. great things that have been accomplished

empire .... large area of power

geometry ..... study of patterns and figures

Read this passage. It is about people who made their own island. Then choose the correct answer for each question.

For hundreds of years, the Incan people oversaw a mighty empire. Huge cities showed the Inca's advanced culture. They knew math, geometry, and astronomy. Their achievements in science and agriculture are well known.

The Incan Empire also had many problems. The Incas took over other people's towns and villages. Often the people would become slaves. They had no rights, and their Incan masters considered them only as property. Many people died from the hard work of building the Incan Empire.

One day, a small group of slaves had had enough. They wanted their freedom. They wanted their own land. But they had no money. All they had was straw. The straw was set under stones to move them for building.

Staring at the straw, someone must have had an idea. He started to weave the straw into a mat. He got help from others, and they wove a very big mat. They added layers to the bottom. They wove the (7)_____ very tight. It was tight enough to hold out water. They must have worked on it in secret. It took a long time, but at last they had a huge (8)_____. It was about the size of a basketball court.

Then the big day came. The people set the mat out on a big lake. They stepped onto the mat and pushed it off shore. They were floating! They had (9)_____ their own island!

The Incas must have thought these people were crazy! It is not known whether they tried to bring them back to land. But the people stayed on the straw island. They made a living with their woven straw boats. They would deliver things from one side of the lake to the other.

The people had to keep adding new layers of straw to their (10)_____. The straw at the bottom was always rotting. But they kept their island afloat. Their freedom was worth all the discomfort and hard work. To this day, people still live on the straw island!

Identifying the Sequence

1 How did the straw island begin?

  A. Someone went to get slaves.
  B. Someone made a straw boat.
  C. Someone wove a mat of straw.
  D. Some made a stone building.

2 What did the people do when the mat was done?

  A. Sold it to the Incas.
  B. Set it in the water.
  C. Hid it from the Incas.
  D. Watched it sink.

Identifying Details

3 The island was made of—

  A. straw
  B. stone
  C. slaves
  D. water

4 The slaves wanted—

  A. money
  B. buildings
  C. freedom
  D. boats

Understanding the Main Idea

5 What is the main idea?

  A. The Incas were mean to their slaves.
  B. The straw island gave the people freedom.
  C. The people on the island had straw boats.
  D. People still live on the straw island.

6 What would be the best title?

  A. The Incan Empire
  B. Living on an Island
  C. Making Straw Boats
  D. The Straw Island

Using the Context

Look back at the passage. Choose the correct word to fill in the blank.

7 A. straw   C. island
  B. stones   D. slaves

8 A. mat   C. straw
  B. boat   D. building

9 A. floated   C. bought
  B. wanted   D. woven

10 A. land   C. boat
   B. island   D. lake

Now use the Answer Key to check your answers. Mark the number you got correct on the Progress Chart.

UNIT 5
LESSON 25

VOCABULARY

dribbling . . . bouncing a ball while running

twilight . . . . . . time just before sundown

Read each passage. Then choose the correct answer.

CLAMMING

Shawn and Jack were staying on the beach. "Let's have clams for dinner," said Jack.

"That sound great," said Shawn. "Should we go to the store for them?"

"Wait and see," said Jack. Soon, the tide went out. There were clams lying all over the sand. "Let's go get dinner," he said.

1 You can tell that—

   A. Shawn doesn't know much about where clams live.

   B. Shawn thinks they will get clams at the store.

   C. Shawn does not know how to cook clams.

   D. Jack does not know much about the water.

2 From the story you can tell that—

   A. Jack and Shawn go to the store.

   B. Jack and Shawn don't eat clams.

   C. Jack wants Shawn to go to the store.

   D. Jack and Shawn will dig for clams.

THE HUNGRY CAMEL

Camels will eat just about anything. They can eat cactuses, bones, and blankets. One man tells about a camel eating his overcoat! No matter what they eat, camels don't get sick.

3 You can tell that—

A. Camels are not very smart.
B. Camels do not see well.
C. Camels don't care what they eat.
D. Camels will eat only clothes.

4 From the story, you can tell that—

A. Camels have strong stomachs.
B. Camels are like people.
C. Camels are very foolish.
D. Camels do not like food.

GOODBYE, BLUE SKY

If there were no air or dust, the sky wouldn't be blue. It would look jet-black. With no dust or air, there would be no twilight. When the sun went down there would not be a sunset.

5 You can tell that—

A. Air and dust are bad for people.
B. Air and dust make things dirty.
C. Air and dust help make the sky blue.
D. We do not need air and dust.

6 You can tell that air and dust—

A. Keep us from getting cold.
B. Help us to see color in the sky.
C. Help us to see distance.
D. Make everything sunny.

THE LONG SHOT

The team was three points behind. Rita dribbled the ball, dodging here and there. She was far from the basket, but she took the shot. She made it! The long shot was worth three points.

7 You can tell that—

A. Rita was playing soccer.
B. Rita was playing football.
C. Rita was playing basketball.
D. Rita was not good at sports.

8 You can tell that Rita's shot—

A. Tied the game.
B. Missed the basket.
C. Was too long.
D. Was not long enough.

SUNFLOWERS

If you watch a field of sunflowers, you will notice something surprising. In the morning, the heads of the flowers face east. As the day goes by, they turn to the west.

9 You can tell that sunflowers—

A. Are very beautiful flowers.
B. Close their blossoms at night.
C. Do not grow quickly.
D. Turn their heads to follow the sun.

10 The sunflowers face east—

A. To see the sun go down.
B. To grow much bigger.
C. To face the sunrise.
D. To grow more quickly.

Now use the Answer Key to check your answers. Mark the number you got correct on the Progress Chart.

LESSON 26

VOCABULARY

invisible . . . cannot be seen
tense . . . . . hold tighter

forecaster . . . . someone who tells what
will happen

Read each passage. Then choose the correct answer.

NEWS ABOUT NAILS

Our fingernails and toenails aren't very useful. We can scratch with our fingernails. The nails protect the tips of our fingers. But toenails do not seem to have any purpose at all.

Fingernails grow about three or four times faster than toenails. The nails on the longest fingers grow the fastest. Nails on the shorter fingers grow more slowly. Both fingernails and toenails grow faster in the summer.

1 You can tell that fingernails—
   A. Have no purpose.
   B. Have two purposes.
   C. Have one purpose.
   D. Are not strong.

2 Fingernails grow fastest on the—
   A. First finger.
   B. Thumb.
   C. Toenails.
   D. Middle finger.

SECRET MESSAGES

You can use invisible ink to write secret messages. Just dip a toothpick in lemon juice or onion juice. Use the toothpick to write your message on paper. Let the juice dry. Send your message to a friend. Your friend can make the secret message appear. All they have to do is hold it up to a hot lightbulb. Then they can write a secret message back!

3 You can tell that—
   A. Invisible ink is hard to make.
   B. Lemon juice is clear.
   C. Most people write with lemon juice.
   D. Most people write secret messages.

4 From the story, you can tell that—
   A. Heat makes the message show up.
   B. Most people write with lemon juice.
   C. It is hard to read a secret message.
   D. Most people write with toothpicks.

PARTLY CLOUDY

Jeff was the weather forecaster on the local radio station. On Sunday, he said that Monday would be partly cloudy.

Monday morning, a woman called the radio station. She asked to speak to the weather forecaster. Jeff got on the phone. The woman said, "I thought you'd like to know something. I just shoveled two feet of 'partly cloudy' off my front steps!"

5 You can tell that—

A. It snowed on Monday.
B. It rained on Monday.
C. It was partly cloudy on Monday.
D. It was sunny on Monday.

6 You can tell that Jeff—

A. Was right about the weather.
B. Was mad at the woman.
C. Was wrong about the weather.
D. Did not care about the weather.

7 You can tell that the woman—

A. Was happy.
B. Was upset.
C. Was funny.
D. Was asleep.

GETTING TO SLEEP

Some people have trouble getting to sleep. How about you? Here is a trick for getting to sleep. Lie down flat. First, tense all the muscles in your feet. Then relax them. Next, do the same with the muscles in your legs. Tense the muscles in your stomach, then let them relax. Do the same with both arms. By now, your arms and legs should feel heavy. Last of all, tense the muscles in your face. Let your jaw go slack. By that time, you should be almost asleep.

8 You can tell that—

A. You have to be tense to go to sleep.
B. You have to be heavy to go to sleep.
C. You have to be relaxed to go to sleep.
D. You have to use your muscles to get to sleep.

9 You can tell that your muscles—

A. Never relax.
B. All relax at the same time.
C. Relax in a certain order.
D. Relax all the time.

10 When your arms and legs feel heavy—

A. They are tense.
B. They are flat.
C. They are awake.
D. They are relaxed.

Now use the Answer Key to check your answers. Mark the number you got correct on the Progress Chart.

UNIT 5
LESSON 27

VOCABULARY

swipe . . . . steal
valuable . . worth a lot

appreciate . . think something is special
groggy . . . . sleepy

Read each passage. Then choose the correct answer for each question.

FLYING CREATURES

There are some creatures that seem to fly. Flying fish and flying squirrels sail through the air. But they are not really flying. They glide on the wind. Flying fish have strong fins that can catch the wind. They can go as far as a quarter of a mile on one glide. They can travel up to 30 miles per hour!

Flying squirrels have a fold of skin under their arms that catch the wind. This skin does not work as well as the fish's fin. They can only glide downward out of trees.

1 You can tell that flying squirrels—

   A. Do not go as far as flying fish.
   B. Are not really squirrels.
   C. Are not as smart as fish.
   D. Can go farther than the fish.

2 You can tell that flying fish—

   A. Are not very smart.
   B. Have wings.
   C. Don't have wings.
   D. Cannot swim.

3 From the story you can tell that—

   A. The fish and squirrels are like birds.
   B. The fish and squirrels cannot swim.
   C. The fish and squirrels appear to fly.
   D. The flying fish hunts the squirrels.

THE GARAGE SALE

Beth and Eric both had lots of old toys. They decided that they were going to have a garage sale on Saturday. They would get rid of their junk and make money at the same time.

They put up signs. Then they spent the next few days getting ready. Beth was trying to price her Raggedy Ann. "This doll is great. It's worth at least 20 dollars," she said to herself.

Eric decided his old matchbox cars were valuable. He marked them at 25 dollars.

On Saturday, Beth and Eric couldn't understand why their toys weren't selling.

"I guess we'll just have to keep this old stuff," said Beth. "No one seems to appreciate it." Eric agreed.

4 You can tell that—

A. Beth still likes her doll.
B. Eric didn't like his toys.
C. Beth doesn't like Eric.
D. Beth wants lots of money.

5 You can tell that—

A. Beth and Eric sold everything.
B. Beth and Eric didn't sell much.
C. Beth and Eric gave things away.
D. Beth though Eric charged too much.

6 You can tell that—

A. Beth and Eric lowered the prices.
B. Beth and Eric made lots of money.
C. The kids were happy to keep their toys.
D. The kids didn't like each other's toys.

THE GRIZZLY

In fall, grizzly bears are busy eating. They walk through the woods looking for berries, mice, fruit, and eggs. They will swipe fish from the streams. Every day, the bears eat as much as they can. They are constantly on the move. Bears need to get as fat as possible. They need to have at least four inches of fat on them.

The days get colder and shorter. The bear starts moving slower. It seems groggy, and drags itself from place to place. Finally, the grizzly crawls into her den. The snow soon covers the entrance. The bear does not leave that den all winter.

7 You can tell that—

A. The grizzly eats this way all year.
B. The grizzly eats this way only in the fall.
C. The grizzly will eat anything.
D. The grizzly does not like to hunt.

8 You can tell that the grizzly—

A. Is getting ready for spring.
B. Likes to eat.
C. Is getting ready for winter.
D. Is going to eat all winter.

9 You can tell that in the winter—

A. The grizzly is always fat.
B. The grizzly doesn't like to eat.
C. The grizzly is always hunting.
D. The grizzly lives off its fat.

10 From the story you can tell that—

A. The grizzly spends the winter outdoors.
B. The grizzly spends the winter sleeping.
C. The grizzly hunts in the snow.
D. The grizzly goes south for the winter.

Now use the Answer Key to check your answers. Mark the number you got correct on the Progress Chart.

LESSON 28

VOCABULARY

realize . . . . . to know something
vaccine . . . . . medicine given with a needle

dedicate . . . . . . give yourself to
nervous system . . the nerves in your body

Read each passage. Then choose the correct answer for each question.

JONAS SALK

Jonas Salk was a curious kid. He liked exploring the world around him. As a baby, his first excited words were "Dirt, dirt!"

Jonas did very well in school. His parents wanted him to become a lawyer. But Jonas soon realized that he wanted to dedicate his life to something else.

When Salk was a boy, there was a terrible flu virus that hit the country. Many people died, including young children. Jonas knew several friends who were killed by the flu. He knew then that he wanted to help find cures for deadly diseases. Salk became a medical researcher.

Salk had his chance to fight a deadly disease. It was called polio (say PO•lee•o). People who got polio often could not walk. Sometimes, they could not breathe. Often they died. Salk found a vaccine for polio. He was a national hero. But he would not take money for the vaccine. He said that it should belong to humanity.

1 You can tell that—

   A. Jonas became interested in the law.
   B. Jonas became interested in medicine.
   C. Jonas decided he wanted to make money.
   D. Jonas did not want to get polio.

2 You can tell that Salk's parents—

   A. Did not want him to go to school.
   B. Wanted to him be a doctor.
   C. Wanted him to be successful.
   D. Wanted him to stay at home.

3 Seeing several friends die made Salk—

   A. Want to help.
   B. Get scared.
   C. Get angry.
   D. Not care.

4 Salk made the polio vaccine because—

   A. He wanted to get rich.
   B. He didn't want to get sick.
   C. He wanted to help people.
   D. He didn't like people.

5 Salk didn't take money for the vaccine—

    A. Because he was not smart.
    B. Because he didn't think it was right.
    C. Because it wasn't important.
    D. Because he was too shy.

IT'S COLD!

Have you ever been out too long on a cold day? Then you probably know about shivering. Your body shakes a little, and sometimes your teeth even chatter. Would you believe that shivering is good for you?

When you shiver, it is a way that your body warms up. How can that be? Your nervous system is sending messages to your muscles. It is telling them to move around. That helps create a little bit of heat.

Shivering is a way for your body to survive very cold weather. But it is still not a good idea to be out in the cold for too long. After awhile, your body stops trying to stay warm. Your hands and feet start to go numb. Then you cannot feel your arms and legs. This is a sign that your body is in danger. Get to shelter as soon as possible!

6 When it is cold, you can tell that—

    A. Your body doesn't care.
    B. Your body doesn't know.
    C. Your body likes to be cold.
    D. Your body tries to stay warm.

7 When you shiver—

    A. Your feet are moving.
    B. You are going to freeze.
    C. Your muscles are moving.
    D. Your brain is moving.

8 Shivering creates—

    A. Cold.
    B. Heat.
    C. Numbness.
    D. Sadness.

9 When your arms get numb—

    A. It is time to shiver.
    B. Your brain doesn't know.
    C. They are getting too warm.
    D. Your body is in trouble.

10 When you get too cold—

    A. Find a place to get warm.
    B. Keep shivering.
    C. Don't think about it.
    D. Your brain will take over.

Now use the Answer Key to check your answers. Mark the number you got correct on the Progress Chart.

LESSON 29

VOCABULARY

mandatory . . . something that must be done

persevered . . . kept trying

ancient . . . . very old

concentrate . . . . to focus

confident . . . . . . sure of yourself

Read each passage. Then choose the correct answer for each question.

MARY MCLEOD BETHANY

Today it is mandatory for all children in the United States go to school. But this was not always true. This was the case in the 1880s in South Carolina, where Mary McLeod lived.

Mary McLeod was one of 17 children. Her whole family had to work hard to make ends meet. Mary dreamed of learning to read. When she was nine, a church opened a school for African-American children. Mr. McLeod could only spare one child. Mary studied hard for the next three years.

There was no high school for African-Americans in the area where Mary lived. A woman gave Mary money so that she could go away to school. She spent the next seven years getting a high school and college education. She decided to devote her life to teaching.

Mary loved teaching, but she had bigger dreams. Finally her dream came true. In Florida she opened a school for girls. She taught 250 African-American girls. It was hard to keep the school open, but they persevered. Mary made a huge

difference for the future of African-American education in this country.

1 You can tell that in the 1880s—

   A. No one ever went to school.
   B. Most children didn't go to school.
   C. There were not many African-American schools.
   D. Mary did not want to go to school.

2 You can tell that Mary—

   A. Wanted to go to school.
   B. Didn't like school.
   C. Wanted to work at home.
   D. Didn't want to go to school.

3 You can tell that Mary's father—

   A. Didn't let Mary go to school.
   B. Didn't want Mary to go to school.
   C. Didn't believe in going to school.
   D. Let Mary go to school.

4 You can tell that Mary—

   A. Was good in school.
   B. Didn't like school.
   C. Liked being at the farm.
   D. Wasn't good at school.

5 You can tell that Mary wanted to—

    A. Own her own farm.
    B. Get married.
    C. Open a school.
    D. Go back home.

KARATE

The word karate (say kuh•RAH•tee) means "empty hand." Is it a sport, a way of fighting, or a philosophy? Karate is actually all of these things.

Karate began over 2,000 years ago. There were monks in India that needed a way to protect themselves. But they did not believe in weapons. The movements of karate use the arms and legs. The motions help a person protect him or herself without hurting the attacker.

Over the years, karate spread to other countries. People in Korea, China, and Japan all studied karate. Each country had a slightly different method. Often the armies in these countries were trained in karate.

After World War II, American soldiers brought karate back home. Now, karate is taught all over the United States. People of all ages study the ancient art.

Some people use karate to get stronger. Young people will often take karate to help them feel more confident. Karate teaches you how to concentrate. That is a useful skill for just about anyone!

6 Karate is called "empty hand" because—

    A. You do not use your hands.
    B. You do not fight with weapons.
    C. It is for people without hands.
    D. It is not really a sport.

7 You can tell that—

    A. Karate is a new sport.
    B. Karate is not a sport.
    C. Karate had been around for a long time.
    D. Karate is not fun for most people.

8 American soldiers must have seen karate—

    A. In America.
    B. In China or Japan.
    C. At home.
    D. 2,000 years ago.

9 You can tell that some people do karate—

    A. To learn to read.
    B. To make new friends.
    C. So they can kick.
    D. For exercise.

10 Karate can help you—

    A. Learn to dance.
    B. Think more clearly.
    C. Make new friends.
    D. Grow longer legs.

Now use the Answer Key to check your answers. Mark the number you got correct on the Progress Chart.

UNIT 5 REVIEW
LESSON 30

VOCABULARY

mission . . . . . special purpose
expeditions . . . trips
abandoned . . . left behind

elevation . . . . . how high something is
summit . . . . the highest point

Read the passage. It is about cleaning up Mount Everest. Then choose the correct answer for each question.

Glen and his friends set up their tents. It was a nice day on Mount Everest. They could see the huge peak towering above them. The friends were there for a special mission. They would climb Mount Everest. Many have tried to get to the top. There have been some successes. But many expeditions have ended in failure.

Glen's group wanted to clean up Mount Everest. Over the last 50 years, more than 15 tons of garbage has been left on the mountain slopes. Everywhere you look there are abandoned tents, stoves, clothes, and food containers. There are bottles that used to hold oxygen.

Why is there so much garbage on Mount Everest? In some cases, it is just because the climbers were not thoughtful. But often these items were left behind by climbers who could not carry them anymore. Many climbers have had to come down the mountain because their health was in danger. They had to leave everything they could not (5)_____ and escape with their lives.

What put these climbers in such danger? It is the mountain itself. Mount Everest is over 29 thousand feet tall. It is the highest mountain in the world. The higher the elevation, the less oxygen there is to breathe. At the camp, Glen has a hard time even getting his shirt on. Every movement is a lot of work. For this reason, many have died trying to scale the summit. Those who were having trouble often left behind most of their gear.

First, Glen's group spends weeks going up and down the slopes of Mount Everest. They pick up garbage and take it down to their camp. Then they will pack it off the mountain. They want to preserve this rare and special environment.

Identifying the Sequence

1 What does Glen's group do first?

   A. Pick up trash on the mountain.
   B. Climb up the mountain and ski.
   C. Climb up the mountain and camp.
   D. Climb down the mountain.

2 What does Glen's group do last?

    A. Put a flag on top of the mountain.
    B. Set up a campsite.
    C. Take the trash down the mountain.
    D. Get their pictures taken.

Identifying Details

3 Mount Everest is—

    A. 10 thousand feet tall
    B. 29 thousand feet tall
    C. one foot tall
    D. one thousand feet tall

4 On Mount Everest there was—

    A. 15 tons of ice
    B. very little trash
    C. 15 tons of trash
    D. very little snow

Using the Context

Look back at the passage. Choose the correct answer.

5 A. trash   C. camp
     B. carry   D. hike

Understanding the Main Idea

6 What is the main idea?

    A. Many people have tried to climb Mount Everest.
    B. People should not climb Mount Everest.
    C. Many mountain climbers are messy.
    D. People are working to clean up

Mount Everest.

7 What would be the best title?

    A. Climbing Mount Everest
    B. Pick Up Your Trash!
    C. Glen's Camping Gear
    D. Cleaning up Mount Everest

Drawing Conclusions

8 From the story you can tell that—

    A. Most people don't make it up Mount Everest.
    B. Most people can hike very well.
    C. Mount Everest is an easy hike.
    D. Most people get to the top of Mount Everest.

9 You can tell that—

    A. Many people have been to the top of Mount Everest.
    B. No one cares about Mount Everest.
    C. Glen cares about Mount Everest.
    D. Glen wants to be famous.

10 You can tell that—

    A. It was hard to get the trash off the mountain.
    B. There is no trash on the mountain.
    C. There is not much to do on Mount Everest.
    D. Mount Everest is a great place to visit.

Now use the Answer Key to check your answers. Mark the number you got correct on the Progress Chart.

UNIT 6
LESSON 31

VOCABULARY

forecast . . . to tell what will happen
racket . . . . a lot of noise

compartment . . . a place to keep things

Read each passage. Then choose the correct answer for each question.

NATURE'S FORECAST

Did you miss the weather forecast on the news? Just look around at nature's weather forecast. Crickets chirp faster when it gets hot. Birds stay out of the sky when a storm is brewing. Is there dew on the grass in the morning? That means it will be a nice day.

1   Which is probably true?

    A. Animals don't care how hot it is.
    B. Insects like cold weather.
    C. Animals know the weather before people do.
    D. People always know the weather.

2   Birds probably—

    A. Don't like hot weather.
    B. Don't want to fly in a storm.
    C. Don't care about the weather.
    D. Like to fly in a storm.

THE VET

Rachel took her cat Max to the vet. They had to wait for a long time. A woman came in with two little dogs. Then a man came in with a big dog. What a racket!

"I'll bring Max back tomorrow," Rachel said.

3 Which is probably true?

    A. The dogs liked Max.
    B. The dogs were quiet.
    C. Max wanted to play.
    D. The dogs barked at each other.

4 Rachel probably decided that—

    A. Max was getting too upset.
    B. Max wanted to play with the dogs.
    C. She didn't like the vet.
    D. She wanted to go shopping instead.

THE BIG MOVE

Marta's family was moving. The whole family would help move things into the new house. But what about the heavy stuff? Marta's parents couldn't do it themselves.

When they pulled up, there was a group of neighbors waiting. They helped get everything moved inside.

5 Which is probably true?

    A. Marta is an adult.
    B. Marta's parents were the only adults.
    C. Marta didn't have much stuff.
    D. Marta's family didn't move.

6 Marta and her family probably—

    A. Didn't like their new neighbors.
    B. Didn't like their new house.
    C. Liked their old house better.
    D. Were glad to get help moving.

THE LIVES OF TREES

How long do most trees live? An apple tree can live for 40 years. A maple tree can live for 50 to 75 years. Some oaks can live as long as 300 years. All of these trees flourish in the right conditions.

The bristlecone pine is an amazing tree. It can live for as long as 4,000 years!

7 Which is probably true?

    A. A maple tree has the shortest life.
    B. An apple tree has the longest life
    C. The bristlecone has the longest life.
    D. Most trees live 100 years.

8 When a tree is planted, it probably—

    A. Needs certain things to do well.
    B. Will probably die soon.
    C. Will live a long time.
    D. Can grow anywhere.

THE MESSY CAR

Tina was looking for her tire gauge in the glove compartment. She took out ten plastic forks and three pair of sunglasses. Some quarters and dimes fell out.

"Where did it go?" Tina muttered.

9 Which is probably true?

    A. Tina has a very neat car.
    B. Tina has a hard time finding things.
    C. Tina has too much stuff in the car.
    D. Tina doesn't have a tire gauge.

10 Which is probably true?
    A. Tina does not need the tire gauge.
    B. Tina needs everything in the glove compartment.
    C. Tina will look in the trunk of the car.
    D. Tina did not find her tire gauge.

Now use the Answer Key to check your answers. Mark the number you got correct on the Progress Chart.

LESSON 32

VOCABULARY

erode . . . . . wear away
scenic . . . . . very beautiful

frigid . . . . . . very cold
navigate . . . . get around

Read each passage. Then choose the correct answer for each question.

FLOWERS WE EAT

When you think of flowers, do you think of cooking ingredients? Most people don't, but many people do cook flowers every day. No, they do not put daisies in their stew, but they might put in some broccoli. Broccoli is a type of flower. So are cabbage and brussel sprouts.

    Some people eat other kinds of flowers, too. You can put flowers in salads. Try some nasturtium (say nas•TUR•shum) petals in a salad. They taste good, and add color to the salad.

1 Which is probably true?

    A. All vegetables are flowers.
    B. Most people don't like flowers.
    C. We eat more flowers than we think.
    D. We should eat only flowers.

2 Which is probably true about flowers?

    A. Many of them could be good to eat.
    B. They are the same as vegetables.
    C. They are not good for people to eat.
    D. They are only for putting in a vase.

THE SLIDING HIGHWAY

There is an unusual place in California. It is right by the ocean. There are many steep cliffs made of soft dirt. Every year, the cliff erodes a little. Whole sections fall into the ocean.

    There is a road on the cliffs that people like to drive on. But it is very narrow. When the hills slide, the road slides, too. The road is always sliding into the ocean! This does not sound very safe. Some people want to move the road somewhere else, but others want to keep the road. It has a very scenic view.

3 Which is probably true about the road?

    A. People don't like to go there.
    B. It is a very dangerous place.
    C. It is easy to drive on.
    D. It is very wide.

4 Which is probably true?

    A. They should move the road.
    B. The road can be made wider.
    C. The hills will stop sliding.
    D. People don't like the road.

POLAR BEARS

Polar bears live in North Pole. The North Pole is a frigid environment with ice and snow everywhere. There are no trees or bushes. How does the polar bear survive such harsh weather?

The polar bear has beautiful white fur. There is also long fur at the bottom of its feet that protects them from the cold. The fur is very stiff on the bear's legs. That helps the bear navigate in the water. Polar bears swim to catch their food. They have adapted well to the cold weather.

5 Which is probably true about the North Pole?

   A. It is easy to live there.
   B. It is fun to drive a car there.
   C. It is hard to find food there.
   D. It is a warm place.

6 Which is probably true about polar bears?

   A. They like to swim.
   B. Their fur is not warm.
   C. They don't like fish.
   D. They don't swim.

7 Which is probably true?

   A. Polar bears like warm weather.
   B. Polar bears like cold weather.
   C. Polar bears don't like ice.
   D. Polar bears are not smart

THE SUMMER STORM

It was a hot, muggy summer day. The Chens were sitting on the back lawn under a tree, trying to stay cool.

Suddenly, Dad pointed at the sky. "Look at all the dark clouds," he exclaimed. "Hurry! We've got to close all the windows." Dad and the kids scattered around to close the windows. Just then it started to pour.

"That was close," said Heather. "Mom will be relieved when she gets home."

8 It is probably true that—

   A. The Chens liked hot weather.
   B. The windows in the house were open.
   C. The windows in the house were shut.
   D. The Chens lived under a tree.

9 It is probably true that Dad—

   A. Liked being outside with the kids.
   B. Didn't want to go inside.
   C. Closed the windows by himself.
   D. Knew it would rain because of the clouds.

10 It is probably true that Mom—

   A. Didn't know it was raining.
   B. Knew the kids would not help.
   C. Was far away from home.
   D. Knew that the windows were open.

Now use the Answer Key to check your answers. Mark the number you got correct on the Progress Chart.

UNIT 6
LESSON 33

VOCABULARY

concentrate . think hard
generated . . to make
petition . . . . a paper that lots of
people have signed

sentries . . . . . guards
turbines . . . . . a place where electricity
is stored
Cambodia . . . . a country in east Asia

Read each passage. Then choose the correct answer for each question.

THE BIG JUMP

Mika turned on the lights in the building. She looked out over the ice, which was smooth and quiet. It was early in the morning and the place was quiet. Mika was glad because she needed to really concentrate today.

She put on all her gear. Then she got out on the ice. She felt her two skate blades cut across the smooth surface. She circled to gain speed. Today she would try a jump she'd never completed before. She circled a few more times to work up her courage. She knew she could do it, but the contest was coming up tomorrow. Would she be ready?

1 Which is probably true?

A. Mika is on a lake.
B. Mika is at a rollerskating rink.
C. Mika is at the ocean.
D. Mika is at an ice rink.

2 Which is probably true?

A. Mika is rollerblading.
B. Mika is ice-skating.
C. Mika is dancing.
D. Mika is doing gymnastics.

3 Which is probably true about Mika?

A. She is not nervous.
B. She does not skate.
C. She is a little nervous.
D. She has done this jump a lot.

WINDMILL POWER

You can see an amazing sight on a ridge outside of San Francisco. You come over a hill and there are all these windmills. They stand straight as sentries. They are scattered across many hillsides. If the wind is blowing, their arms are spinning. In a breeze, they go slowly. Sometimes they whiz like helicopter blades.

The windmills generate electricity from the wind. The power is stored in turbines at the base of each windmill. They are linked in a central network. The community can take electricity from that network at any time.

4 Which is probably true?

   A. The windmills need a strong wind to work.
   B. Strong wind makes the windmills go fast.
   C. The windmills are like helicopters.
   D. The windmills have to go slowly.

5 Which is probably true about windmills?

   A. They are hard to take care of.
   B. They are hard to build.
   C. They need to be built in a windy place.
   D. They do not need wind to work.

6 Which is probably true?

   A. Power is stored in the windmill network.
   B. Windmills are not reliable.
   C. Windmills are very out of date.
   D. Power is stored at the windmill.

THEY CALL HIM LUCKY

There were some brave kids in Cambodia. They heard that a man wanted to take an orphaned baby elephant out of the zoo. It was a rare rainforest elephant. The man collected wild animals. He pulled a lot of strings to get the baby elephant.

Some junior high kids heard about the baby elephant. They knew that the elephant would not get good care. They wrote up a petition. They spread it around to kids all over their city. The word got out. Soon, kids from all over were writing to save the elephant.

The petition worked! The elephant stayed at the zoo. She got good care and a lot of love. The kids named her Lucky.

7 Which is probably true?

   A. The baby elephant was in danger.
   B. The baby elephant was too big.
   C. The zoo did not want the elephant.
   D. The baby elephant liked the man.

8 Which is probably true about the elephant?

   A. He had parents.
   B. His mother had died.
   C. He didn't like people.
   D. He lived with other elephants.

9 Which is probably true about the kids?

   A. They wanted to own the elephant.
   B. They wanted to be famous.
   C. They didn't care about animals.
   D. They cared a lot about animals.

10 The elephant was probably named Lucky because—

   A. No one liked him.
   B. He liked the zoo.
   C. He was lucky to be alive.
   D. It is a funny name.

Now use the Answer Key to check your answers. Mark the number you got correct on the Progress Chart.

LESSON 34

VOCABULARY

preserve . . . a place where animals are kept safe

habitat . . . . a place where an animal lives

military . . . . . the part of the goverment that protects the country

campaign . . . . a planned action

contribute . . . give

Read each passage. Then choose the correct answer for each question.

KEEPERS OF THE CREEK

In Alaska, a group of students ride down the creek. They have adopted this creek. They are working to preserve a salmon habitat.

The creek is a pathway for wild salmon to swim. There are not many creeks or rivers where salmon can swim freely. But even here, the salmon are in danger.

Wildlife feeds on the salmon. But there is a bigger threat. Young salmon need shady, cool water. When people walk along the creek banks they trample the overhanging plants. Too many boats dig up the dirt at the creek bottom.

The students go every year to test the water. They want to make sure it is clean enough for the salmon. They write stories and articles. They do as much as they can to get the word out.

1 Which is probably true?

   A. Students fish on the creek.

   B. The students like to go rafting.

   C. The students go to the creek every year.

   D. The students have been to the creek once.

2 Which is probably true?

   A. Humans take good care of salmon.

   B. Humans do not like to eat fish.

   C. Wildlife eat all the fish.

   D. Humans are a big threat to salmon.

3 Which is probably true?

   A. The students like to catch salmon.

   B. The students care about the salmon.

   C. The students want to live in a city.

   D. The students want to be famous.

TUBING

Have you ever gone tubing? First you get an old tube from inside a truck tire. These are called innertubes.

Take your innertube to a small river or creek.You should also wear a life jacket.

You should not try to go down a narrow place in the river. The water could be too fast. Look for a wide place in the river. Then you can have a nice, peaceful ride.

It is important to innertube with friends. It is a great way to spend a day. Be sure and bring your sunscreen, too!

4 Which is probably true about innertubes?

    A. They are filled with air.
    B. They are heavy because they came off trucks.
    C. They are not comfortable to sit on.
    D. They could sink in the river.

5 Which is probably true?

    A. Innertubes will not flip over.
    B. Innertubes are a lot like boats.
    C. Innertubes could flip over in fast water.
    D. Innertubes are made of chains.

6 Which is probably true about a river?

    A. In a narrow part the water goes slow.
    B. In a narrow part the water goes fast.
    C. In a wide part the water goes fast.
    D. It is not good for tubing.

7 Which is probably true about innertubing?

    A. It should not be done in water.
    B. It is a costly sport.
    C. It is done mainly by truck drivers.
    D. It can be dangerous.

RECYCLING FOR YOUR COUNTRY

In the 1940s, Americans went on a huge recycling campaign. But most people didn't think about it that way. They were recycling for their country.

World War II was going on. The military needed metal, rubber, and paper. They put out a call to all Americans. People brought in old tires and cars. These were used to make boats and airplanes and jeeps.

Americans also gave up a lot of things to help their country. Gas and food were rationed. There was no chewing gum because it has a little bit of rubber in it! Most kids said they did not mind contributing something for their country.

8 Which was probably true in the 1940s?

    A. Americans didn't recycle.
    B. Americans did not know they were recycling.
    C. Americans did not want to help the war effort.
    D. Americans wanted to get more cars.

9 Which is probably true?

    A. Old cars were used to make boats.
    B. People were paid for their old cars.
    C. People wanted their old cars back.
    D. People wanted to own new jeeps.

10 Why was there no chewing gum during the war?

    A. The gum did not taste good anymore.
    B. The kids chewed too much gum.
    C. They needed the rubber in the gum.
    D. They sent the gum to the soldiers.

Now use the Answer Key to check your answers. Mark the number you got correct on the Progress Chart.

UNIT 6
LESSON 35

VOCABULARY

valued . . . . thought to be important

heritage . . . stories and customs from the past

recharged . . get more energy

ancestors . . . . relatives that lived long ago

access . . . . . . to get to

Read each passage. Then choose the correct answer for each question.

MAXINE HONG KINGSTON

Maxine Hong Kingston's parents came to America from China. They wanted to build a new life. Maxine's father worked hard to get to California. Later he sent for his wife. Maxine was born soon after.

Maxine grew up in a Chinese neighborhood. Some of the adults spoke a little English at their jobs. But people wanted to keep their culture alive in this strange new land.

Maxine spoke Chinese at home. She also spoke English at school. She loved many things about America. Yet she also valued her Chinese heritage. Maxine felt that she lived in between two very separate worlds.

When she grew up, Maxine became a writer. She wrote about growing up Chinese in America. She told stories to honor her Chinese ancestors. She also told her own story as an American girl. Maxine's book was called *The Woman Warrior*.

1   Which is probably true?

   A. Maxine's father came to America first.
   B. Maxine's mother came to America first.
   C. Maxine's father was born in America.
   D. Maxine was born in China.

2   Which was probably true about Maxine's neighborhood?

   A. No one could speak English.
   B. No one spoke Chinese at home.
   C. No one spoke to Americans
   D. No one spoke English at home.

3   Which is probably true about Maxine?

   A. She learned English in school.
   B. She did not want to learn English.
   C. She learned Chinese at school.
   D. She spoke Chinese at school.

4   Which is probably true?

   A. Maxine wanted to write books in Chinese.

B. Maxine felt she was both American and Chinese.

C. Maxine felt that she was mostly Chinese.

D. Maxine felt that she was mostly American.

5 Which is probably true about Maxine's book?

A. She wrote it in Chinese.

B. She wrote it when she was a girl.

C. She wrote it in English.

D. She wrote it in English and Chinese.

CD BOOKS

Jan spreads her towel on the beach and gets out her book. But her book is not a "book" at all! She opens up a slim laptop. It is about the size of a large book. She turns it on and there is her story!

This scene is not as far off as some may think. Many people predict that computers will one day replace books altogether. After all, one CD-ROM disk can hold as much information as several books. A CD can be accessed at the touch of a button. But can a computer replace the experience of reading a book?

Computers get smaller and lighter every day. Think about all the books you carry at once! And just think of the number of trees you can save!

On the other hand, computers still need to be plugged in somewhere. Laptops have batteries that are easily recharged. But what if your computer book shuts down just as you're getting to the most exciting part?

Whether you like it or not, CD books are on their way.

6 Which is probably true?

A. Jan was reading a magazine.

B. Jan was going to take a nap.

C. Jan was reading on a computer.

D. Jan was reading a book.

7 Which could you probably do with a computer book?

A. Take several books on vacation.

B. Take it on a hike that lasts a month.

C. Take one book chapter on vacation.

D. Use it to plan your trip.

8 What could you probably not do with a computer book?

A. Take it on a hike that lasts a month.

B. Take several books on vacation.

C. Put all your school books on it.

D. Plan your vacation with it.

9 Which is probably true about books?

A. They are not easy to carry.

B. They are printed on paper.

C. They need batteries.

D. They are not fun to read.

10 Which is probably true?

A. There will never be computer books.

B. People will never like computer books.

C. People will only read computer books.

D. Computer books are coming soon.

Now use the Answer Key to check your answers. Mark the number you got correct on the Progress Chart.

LESSON 36

VOCABULARY

ceremony . . a special service
tribal . . . . . part of a tribe or group
dramatic . . exciting

council . . . . . a group that makes decisions
adze . . . . a special carving tool

Read the passage. Then choose the correct answer for each question.

David helps his dad in the workshop. There is the sound of a chainsaw running. David doesn't use the sharp tools. He does help his father with drawing and painting. What are they making? David's dad is a totem pole carver. He is getting ready for a big ceremony.

David's dad has been working on this pole for months. He starts by talking to the people who want the totem pole made. They are the tribal council of the Klallum Indians. They will put the pole in front of their community center. It should tell the story of their people. Then he draws a sketch of the pole. It has animals and fantastic creatures sitting on top of each other. The council agrees to the design.

Then David's dad goes out into the forest. He looks for the straightest tree he can find. He chooses just the right tree, and cuts it down.

In the workshop, he draws the main design. David helps him after school. Finally, the pole is ready to be carved. David's dad gets out the chainsaw and makes the big cuts.

In the old days, that work would have been done by hand. A special chisel called an adze has been used to carve totem poles for hundreds of years. David's dad uses it to carve the smaller details of the pole. He (6)_____ a pair of eyes, a bird's beak, or a bear's snout. The faces look dramatic.

David helps his father finish the painting. Then the pole is done! They will take it to the ceremony next week. David is very excited. He gets to help his dad with the pole-standing dance.

David and his dad stand at the base of the pole. They wear bright red capes with feather headdresses. David's father begins to dance. David knows these steps, too. The dance tells the story of the pole.

The pole stands strong and proud. It is a true work of art. David's dad says that he helped make it great.

Identifying the Sequence

1 What did David's father do first?

    A. Carved the pole.
    B. Chose the tree.
    C. Drew the design.
    D. Painted the pole.

2 What did David's dad do last?

    A. Chose the tree.
    B. Drew the design.
    C. Painted the pole.
    D. Put up the pole.

Identifying Details

3 David's father carves—

    A. animals
    B. totem poles
    C. birds
    D. bears

4 David helped his dad—

    A. carve the pole
    B. chose the tree
    C. plan the design
    D. paint the faces

Using the Context

Look back at the passage. Choose the correct word.

5 A. paints   C. adze
    B. chisels   D. thinks

Understanding the Main Idea

6 What is the main idea?

    A. David's dad likes trees.
    B. Totem poles are hard to make.
    C. David does not like totem poles.
    D. David likes to help his dad make totem poles.

7 What would be the best title?

    A. Using a Chainsaw
    B. Learning to Carve
    C. The Totem Pole Carver
    D. David Dances

Drawing Conclusions

8 You can tell that—

    A. David is bored with totem poles.
    B. David can carve totem poles.
    C. David's dad is an artist.
    D. David's dad is a lawyer.

Making Inferences

9 David and his dad probably—

    A. Are not Native Americans.
    B. Like doing things together.
    C. Do not like art.
    D. Don't do much together.

10 Which is probably true?

    A. David's dad is Native American.
    B. David's dad likes to cut down trees.
    C. David doesn't want to help his dad.
    D. David is an adult.

Now use the Answer Key to check your answers. Mark the number you got correct on the Progress Chart.

ANSWER SHEET

Name _____

Unit # _____ Skill _____

Lesson # _____

1. Ⓐ Ⓑ Ⓒ Ⓓ
2. Ⓐ Ⓑ Ⓒ Ⓓ
3. Ⓐ Ⓑ Ⓒ Ⓓ
4. Ⓐ Ⓑ Ⓒ Ⓓ
5. Ⓐ Ⓑ Ⓒ Ⓓ
6. Ⓐ Ⓑ Ⓒ Ⓓ
7. Ⓐ Ⓑ Ⓒ Ⓓ
8. Ⓐ Ⓑ Ⓒ Ⓓ
9. Ⓐ Ⓑ Ⓒ Ⓓ
10. Ⓐ Ⓑ Ⓒ Ⓓ

Lesson # _____

1. Ⓐ Ⓑ Ⓒ Ⓓ
2. Ⓐ Ⓑ Ⓒ Ⓓ
3. Ⓐ Ⓑ Ⓒ Ⓓ
4. Ⓐ Ⓑ Ⓒ Ⓓ
5. Ⓐ Ⓑ Ⓒ Ⓓ
6. Ⓐ Ⓑ Ⓒ Ⓓ
7. Ⓐ Ⓑ Ⓒ Ⓓ
8. Ⓐ Ⓑ Ⓒ Ⓓ
9. Ⓐ Ⓑ Ⓒ Ⓓ
10. Ⓐ Ⓑ Ⓒ Ⓓ

Lesson # _____

1. Ⓐ Ⓑ Ⓒ Ⓓ
2. Ⓐ Ⓑ Ⓒ Ⓓ
3. Ⓐ Ⓑ Ⓒ Ⓓ
4. Ⓐ Ⓑ Ⓒ Ⓓ
5. Ⓐ Ⓑ Ⓒ Ⓓ
6. Ⓐ Ⓑ Ⓒ Ⓓ
7. Ⓐ Ⓑ Ⓒ Ⓓ
8. Ⓐ Ⓑ Ⓒ Ⓓ
9. Ⓐ Ⓑ Ⓒ Ⓓ
10. Ⓐ Ⓑ Ⓒ Ⓓ

Lesson # _____

1. Ⓐ Ⓑ Ⓒ Ⓓ
2. Ⓐ Ⓑ Ⓒ Ⓓ
3. Ⓐ Ⓑ Ⓒ Ⓓ
4. Ⓐ Ⓑ Ⓒ Ⓓ
5. Ⓐ Ⓑ Ⓒ Ⓓ
6. Ⓐ Ⓑ Ⓒ Ⓓ
7. Ⓐ Ⓑ Ⓒ Ⓓ
8. Ⓐ Ⓑ Ⓒ Ⓓ
9. Ⓐ Ⓑ Ⓒ Ⓓ
10. Ⓐ Ⓑ Ⓒ Ⓓ

Lesson # _____

1. Ⓐ Ⓑ Ⓒ Ⓓ
2. Ⓐ Ⓑ Ⓒ Ⓓ
3. Ⓐ Ⓑ Ⓒ Ⓓ
4. Ⓐ Ⓑ Ⓒ Ⓓ
5. Ⓐ Ⓑ Ⓒ Ⓓ
6. Ⓐ Ⓑ Ⓒ Ⓓ
7. Ⓐ Ⓑ Ⓒ Ⓓ
8. Ⓐ Ⓑ Ⓒ Ⓓ
9. Ⓐ Ⓑ Ⓒ Ⓓ
10. Ⓐ Ⓑ Ⓒ Ⓓ

Lesson # _____

1. Ⓐ Ⓑ Ⓒ Ⓓ
2. Ⓐ Ⓑ Ⓒ Ⓓ
3. Ⓐ Ⓑ Ⓒ Ⓓ
4. Ⓐ Ⓑ Ⓒ Ⓓ
5. Ⓐ Ⓑ Ⓒ Ⓓ
6. Ⓐ Ⓑ Ⓒ Ⓓ
7. Ⓐ Ⓑ Ⓒ Ⓓ
8. Ⓐ Ⓑ Ⓒ Ⓓ
9. Ⓐ Ⓑ Ⓒ Ⓓ
10. Ⓐ Ⓑ Ⓒ Ⓓ

PROGRESS CHART

Lesson #	0	1	2	3	4	5	6	7	8	9	10
Lesson #	0	1	2	3	4	5	6	7	8	9	10
Lesson #	0	1	2	3	4	5	6	7	8	9	10
Lesson #	0	1	2	3	4	5	6	7	8	9	10
Lesson #	0	1	2	3	4	5	6	7	8	9	10
Lesson #	0	1	2	3	4	5	6	7	8	9	10
Review Lesson #	0	1	2	3	4	5	6	7	8	9	10

ANSWER KEY

UNIT 1—IDENTIFYING THE SEQUENCE

Unit 1 Lesson 1	Unit 1 Lesson 2	Unit 1 Lesson 3
1. B	1. D	1. B
2. D	2. C	2. C
3. A	3. B	3. B
4. B	4. D	4. C
5. B	5. A	5. D
6. D	6. C	6. A
7. C	7. B	7. B
8. B	8. B	8. A
9. A	9. A	9. B
10. C	10. D	10. C

Unit 1 Lesson 4	Unit 1 Lesson 5	Unit 1 Lesson 6
1. C	1. B	1. C
2. B	2. D	2. C
3. A	3. C	3. B
4. B	4. A	4. A
5. C	5. B	5. B
6. D	6. D	6. D
7. B	7. A	7. A
8. A	8. C	8. D
9. C	9. A	9. C
10. C	10. C	10. B

UNIT 2—IDENTIFYING DETAILS

Unit 2 Lesson 7	Unit 2 Lesson 8	Unit 2 Lesson 9
1. A	1. D	1. B
2. B	2. C	2. C
3. D	3. A	3. D
4. A	4. B	4. D
5. C	5. C	5. A
6. A	6. A	6. C
7. B	7. B	7. B
8. D	8. D	8. A
9. B	9. A	9. D
10. A	10. C	10. B

Unit 2 Lesson 10	Unit 2 Lesson 11	Unit 2 Lesson 12
1. B	1. C	1. D
2. A	2. B	2. B
3. D	3. D	3. C
4. B	4. B	4. D
5. A	5. A	5. A
6. C	6. C	6. C
7. B	7. A	7. B
8. D	8. D	8. C
9. C	9. B	9. A
10. A	10. D	10. C

UNIT 3—UNDERSTANDING THE MAIN IDEA

Unit 3 Lesson 13	Unit 3 Lesson 14	Unit 3 Lesson 15
1. B	1. B	1. A
2. A	2. C	2. B
3. C	3. D	3. C
4. B	4. C	4. C
5. C	5. B	5. D
6. D	6. B	6. B
7. D	7. C	7. A
8. B	8. D	8. B
9. C	9. B	9. C
10. A	10. A	10. D

Unit 3 Lesson 16	Unit 3 Lesson 17	Unit 3 Lesson 18
1. C	1. A	1. B
2. B	2. C	2. A
3. A	3. A	3. D
4. C	4. C	4. C
5. D	5. B	5. B
6. B	6. B	6. C
7. A	7. D	7. B
8. D	8. D	8. A
9. C	9. A	9. D
10. D	10. C	10. C

UNIT 4—USING THE CONTEXT

Unit 4 Lesson 19	Unit 4 Lesson 20	Unit 4 Lesson 21
1. A	1. A	1. B
2. D	2. D	2. A
3. B	3. C	3. C
4. A	4. A	4. B
5. C	5. A	5. C
6. A	6. C	6. A
7. B	7. D	7. D
8. C	8. B	8. C
9. D	9. A	9. B
10. B	10. B	10. D

Unit 4 Lesson 22	Unit 4 Lesson 23	Unit 4 Lesson 24
1. B	1. B	1. C
2. A	2. D	2. B
3. B	3. C	3. A
4. C	4. D	4. C
5. C	5. A	5. B
6. D	6. B	6. D
7. B	7. B	7. B
8. A	8. C	8. A
9. D	9. A	9. D
10. C	10. C	10. C

UNIT 5—DRAWING CONCLUSIONS

Unit 5 Lesson 25	Unit 5 Lesson 26	Unit 5 Lesson 27
1. B	1. B	1. A
2. D	2. D	2. C
3. C	3. B	3. C
4. A	4. A	4. A
5. C	5. A	5. B
6. B	6. C	6. D
7. C	7. B	7. B
8. A	8. C	8. C
9. D	9. B	9. D
10. C	10. D	10. B

Unit 5 Lesson 28	Unit 5 Lesson 29	Unit 5 Lesson 30
1. B	1. C	1. A
2. C	2. A	2. C
3. A	3. D	3. B
4. C	4. A	4. C
5. B	5. C	5. B
6. D	6. B	6. D
7. C	7. C	7. D
8. B	8. B	8. A
9. D	9. D	9. C
10. A	10. B	10. A

UNIT 6—MAKING INFERENCES

Unit 6 Lesson 31	Unit 6 Lesson 32	Unit 6 Lesson 33
1. C	1. C	1. D
2. B	2. A	2. B
3. D	3. B	3. C
4. A	4. A	4. A
5. B	5. C	5. C
6. D	6. A	6. A
7. C	7. B	7. A
8. A	8. B	8. B
9. C	9. D	9. D
10. D	10. D	10. C

Unit 6 Lesson 34	Unit 6 Lesson 35	Unit 6 Lesson 36
1. C	1. A	1. B
2. D	2. D	2. D
3. B	3. A	3. B
4. A	4. B	4. D
5. C	5. C	5. A
6. B	6. C	6. D
7. D	7. A	7. C
8. B	8. A	8. C
9. A	9. B	9. B
10. C	10. D	10. A